seeing Digital

seeing Digital

a visual guide to the
INDUSTRIES,
ORGANIZATIONS,
& CAREERS
of the
2020s

Published by DXC Technology
DXC Technology
1775 Tysons Blvd.
Tysons, VA 22102 USA
www.dxc.technology

© 2018 by Leading Edge Forum
www.leadingedgeforum.com

ISBN: 978-0-692-11344-8

To all the unseen programmers, engineers, and technicians who make the digital world appear to run so smoothly

Table of Contents

Foreword

Mike Lawrie, Chairman, President, and CEO, DXC Technology

Introduction

Part I – The Post-Cloud Technology Landscape

Part II – The Digital Transformation Journey

Part III – Global Strategies and Competition

Conclusion

Index

Foreword

Mike Lawrie, Chairman, President, and CEO, DXC Technology

For many years, *open source* projects have defied the skeptics, and proved to be a powerful way to accelerate technology innovation. Today, business leaders are increasingly deciding that their intellectual property (IP) shouldn't always be hidden away, only to be made available to a chosen few. Sometimes, IP needs to go where the people are so that it can be leveraged, improved, and reach a critical mass of usage.

That's why DXC Technology is now making our proprietary research and analysis publicly available. We believe that the more clearly our clients, partners, employees, and the wider business ecosystem understand the digital world before us, the greater the benefits for us all. In this sense, *Seeing Digital* can be viewed as DXC's contribution to the digital transformation mindset that so many organizations need today.

In this brief foreword, I will share my personal observations regarding the technology challenges faced by large enterprises today, as well as the lessons learned during our own transformation journey. In both areas, the ideas, insights, and frameworks in this book have sharpened our thinking and focus. I believe they can do the same for you.

Today's enterprise transformation challenge

Business leaders tend to be optimistic about the future. They see globalization expanding their marketplaces, technology creating new opportunities, and rising living standards sustaining a strong economic climate. But whether we are working with clients in banking, healthcare, insurance, aerospace, manufacturing, government, or other sectors, I consistently hear about three main challenges:

1. **Relentless cost pressure.** Large businesses and government agencies could not operate on the scale they do without computer automation. But automation tends to build upon itself, and organizations must become ever-more efficient not only to compete but to survive in today's global marketplace. The intense emphasis on lower costs at every level of the enterprise often puts great strain on day-to-day operations.

2. **'Re-platformed' operations.** Traditional organization structures are being bypassed by integrated, intelligent digital *platforms* that enable the intuitive online experiences that customers and employees have come to expect. However, most of our clients are still in the midst of this shift, with one foot

planted in each world. Moving to a truly *digital-first* operating model can be a highly complex process of business and cultural change.

3. **Designed-in agility.** Most executives can easily imagine a radically transformed digital future, but most also find it hard to gauge the actual extent and speed of change. They are looking for ways to ensure that today's tactical technology decisions support the agility they know they will eventually need.

Few organizations believe they can meet these challenges entirely on their own, which is why even the largest firms choose to work with a best-of-breed network of business partners, leveraging the knowledge and experience of those who have been there before.

Transformation at DXC

Our company has been going through its own transformation journey. It's no secret that in recent years, the IT services industry has been shifting away from large-scale outsourcing – sometimes described as 'your mess for less' – to a business characterized by strategic partnerships that help clients develop seamlessly connected digital systems that lower costs, improve the customer experience, and enable new forms of business innovation.

Like many of our clients, DXC Technology has approached its transformation challenge in two main phases:

1. **Getting fit.** At the former CSC, we launched a multi-year transformation effort that emphasized streamlining and standardizing business operations, revitalizing our internal talent base, carefully selecting partnerships, and significantly lowering overall costs. While these changes were difficult – and often painful – they were the only way to get our company prepared for the future we envisioned.

2. **Scaling for the future.** Once we were sufficiently fit and focused, we were ready to enhance our capabilities and scale our operations to drive growth. We started with point acquisitions in key industries (such as insurance) and practice areas (such as service management). Then, in April 2017, we merged CSC with the Enterprise Services business of Hewlett Packard Enterprise, creating today's $25 billion, 150,000-employee DXC Technology – with the vision, people, and resources needed to help our clients thrive on change.

While we still have a great deal of work to do, being aligned with, and prepared for, the digital future is the right path for transformational success. Just about every company and government agency we work with is now facing some version of this challenge.

Lessons learned

Having experienced the business transformation process several times over the years, I'm often asked what lessons I have learned. My answer is that whether we are talking about individual careers, our clients, or our own firm, I see the same three needs:

1. **Understanding and empathy.** Almost everything starts with strong *situational awareness* – the ability to listen, see, and acknowledge reality, as well as the willingness to put yourself fully in the customer's shoes.

2. **Sensing and learning.** To thrive over the longer term, organizations and individuals must anticipate how the big picture is changing, and then be ready to act when the time comes. This requires a skill set that is continually refreshed, as new digital capabilities and practices emerge.

3. **Conviction and stamina.** Business transformation is hard work. Leaders at every level must establish a clear direction, and then stick to it by making tough decisions. But none of this will matter unless leaders also have the energy, drive, and agility to get the details right and sustain a long-term process of change. There is almost never a quick fix.

Since joining the former CSC as CEO back in 2012, I've seen many times how our research and thought leadership arm, the *Leading Edge Forum* (LEF), has helped our people and our clients in all three of these areas. LEF has enabled us to better visualize and communicate the many changes that surround us. It has identified key market and value chain shifts well before they hit the knee of the curve. Perhaps most importantly, LEF has highlighted the importance of sustained digital leadership at every level of the organization.

In short, LEF has been the tip of the DXC Technology spear. Its research and ideas have played an essential role in our transformation journey, and we think it can help in yours too.

Next-generation challenges

I have always felt profoundly fortunate to have had so much of my journey coincide with the growth of the information technology business. This remarkable industry has provided all the challenges, opportunities, inspiration of colleagues, and sense of purpose one could ask for.

And yet, the most exciting years clearly are ahead. Science, knowledge, and technology are now being systematically brought to bear on just about every human activity, creating entirely new industries and careers, destined to be led by a new generation of tech-savvy and globally minded individuals from every corner of the world. The ability to personalize education can make it possible for each of us to create the life we want to lead.

But of course, we know that there are challenges that come with today's hyper-connectivity and intense global competition. Our industry needs to better demonstrate how digital technology is addressing important societal concerns such as lifting up the developing world, improving the environment, reducing inequality, raising the level of public discourse, and modernizing our energy, transportation, healthcare, agricultural, and other systems.

These will be among the great transformation demands of the 21st century. I am confident that in meeting them, tomorrow's leaders will embrace digital technologies far more than they will fear them, and that the information technology industry will continue to be a highly rewarding place to work and contribute. I am also confident that as the multiple transformations of the decade ahead begin to unfold, the digital dynamics presented in this book will help readers better envision and prepare for these challenges.

Mike Lawrie, Chairman, President, and CEO
DXC Technology

Introduction

What do our clients want to know?

In this chapter

- CEOs ask: Are we getting digital right?

- Silicon Valley asks: Can we pull off our *dual disruption* agenda?

- IT professionals ask: What does our future look like?

- Individuals ask: What does technology mean for me and my career?

- Governments ask: What do these changes mean for our society?

- An increasingly intelligent digital *Matrix* underlies these questions

- This book helps you *see* the *triple transformation* – of industries, organizations, and careers

---

As a $25 billion global IT services provider, DXC Technology works with thousands of large businesses and government agencies all around the world, engaging with CEOs, COOs, CIOs, digital marketing teams, product innovation groups, IT and HR professionals, business strategists, technology suppliers, venture capitalists, government officials, and other digital enthusiasts.

While these groups have very different interests, most have one need in common: they want to better understand the digital future, but they have too much to read already. In recent years, DXC's thought leadership arm, Leading Edge Forum (LEF), has addressed this challenge by taking a highly visual approach. Our clients tell us that our use of pictures conveys ideas, concepts, and decision-making models more quickly and powerfully than the written word alone.

This book seeks to bring our visual approach to a much wider audience. Each of the following 200 or so pages presents a standalone framework, model, scenario, or other image, designed to be useful in its own right. But collectively, they address the questions, dynamics, and transformations listed above, and as briefly summarized in this introduction.

Because the thinking and advice that follows have been drawn from the ongoing work of the entire DXC/LEF research team, this book is written in the voice of *we*. We hope it helps you see the intelligent digital world that is now emerging, and become better prepared for the industries, organizations, and careers of the 2020s – and beyond.

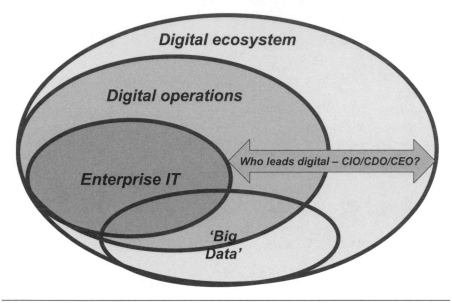

The technology world is full of uncertainties, and the most important ones wind up on the CEO's desk. While most CEOs believe in an increasingly digital future, they often wonder if they're doing the right things and have the right teams and strategies in place. Many senior executives feel that their organizations must undergo a *digital transformation*, even if they aren't always sure what this means.

Not surprisingly, most CEOs look first to their Chief Information Officer (or equivalent) for digital leadership, and this works well in many organizations. But in many others, the CIO is seen as too internally focused, or simply too busy keeping Enterprise IT's house in order. In such cases, marketing executives, business unit owners, COOs, and others often seek to fill the digital leadership void.

But relying on the existing senior leadership team raises its own challenges. Is this group sufficiently tech-savvy? What happens if they have sharply different opinions about the digital future? Who is ultimately responsible for the technology-driven agenda of the firm? These questions often lead to political drama inside the C-suite when important decisions need to be made.

In recent years, many firms have appointed *Chief Digital Officers*. While CDOs are certainly no panacea, their emergence speaks to the perceived digital leadership need in many large companies and government agencies today. Chapters 4, 5, 6, 7, 8, and 10 can help firms address this challenge through a range of organizational, cultural, and team-based approaches.

Silicon Valley asks: Can we pull off our *dual disruption* agenda?

Technology disruptions	*Industry-specific disruptions*
• Cloud, SaaS	• Cars – shared, electric, self-driving
• Mobility, apps	• Banking – advice, lending, Bitcoin
• Social, P2P	• Health – self-service, diagnoses, IoT
• Open source	• Insurance – personalized, algorithmic
• Big Data, analytics	• Manufacturing – robotics, 3D printing
• Sensors, wearables, IoT	• Retail – Amazon, no inventory, China
• Speech, facial recognition	• Education – MOOCs, flipped classes
• AR/VR/3D/AI/machine intelligence	• Legal – smart contracts, digital truth

While CEOs ponder the firm's digital future, Silicon Valley (and its global rivals) are busy building it.

Of course, Silicon Valley has long been the capital of the IT world. It dominates the market for computer hardware, software, networking equipment, data storage, semiconductors, and internet services. 'The Valley' expects this dominance to continue through the *technology disruptions* listed on the left side of the figure.

Indeed, rightly or wrongly, this success is now largely taken for granted. The big question in the Valley today is whether its technology leadership can be extended to the *industry-specific disruptions* listed on the right side of the figure. This is what we mean when we say that Silicon Valley now has a *dual disruption* agenda. Whether the Valley can pull off this agenda will be the main focus of Chapters 1, 2, and 3.

But no matter how these issues ultimately play out, it's clear that the mission of Silicon Valley has expanded. The IT industry grew up as essentially an *arms merchant*, selling its products to anyone who wanted to buy them, but today it is also an *invading army*, often competing against the very companies it supplies.

While Silicon Valley – and especially Google, Apple, Facebook, Amazon, and Microsoft – look invincible today, history cautions otherwise. China, India, and more open, peer-to-peer models will likely challenge today's leaders, as we will discuss in Chapters 3 and 11.

IT professionals ask: What does our future look like?

Value through *back-office* *IT provision*		*Value through* *front-of-the-firm* *digital leadership*
• *Inside-out*		• *Outside-in*
• Cost efficiency		• Business impact
• Standard platforms		• New ways of working
• Service provider		• Agent of change
• IT budgets		• Digital business

Enterprise IT professionals face a very different set of challenges than CEOs and Silicon Valley. On the one hand, they are asked to provide their organization's back-office IT infrastructure and technology processes, with the goal of assuring control, reliability, and efficiency. This requires an inward-looking and risk-averse culture.

But the wider IT industry is driven more by the exciting possibilities on the right side of the figure, and it is only natural that IT professionals would prefer to spend the bulk of their time in these front-of-the-firm digital business realms. However, these missions require an external outlook and a culture of risk-taking.

We use the metaphor of the ancient Roman God Janus to capture this two-headed dilemma. Janus was believed to be able to see equally clearly into the past and the future, and this is a good description of the challenge faced by IT professionals today.

Unfortunately, the demands on the left side of the Janus are often so intense that the right side doesn't get the attention it should, and this is a major source of frustration for many IT professionals. It also explains why *the future of the IT organization* is such a perennial technology industry topic. Chapters 4 through 8 will help firms cope with these internal and external challenges. We will see that moving to the right side of the Janus is a good working definition of what many people mean by *IT transformation*.

Individuals ask: What does technology mean for me and my career?

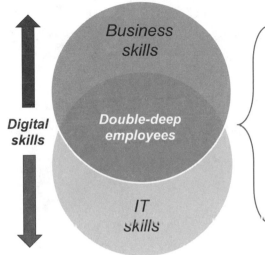

Digital skills

Business skills

Double-deep employees

IT skills

Those individuals that can combine strong digital skills with deep functional expertise are in most demand in just about every field. The demand for 'single-deep' employees and professionals is often in decline.

When you read, watch, or listen to the mainstream media today, you might think that all the traditional jobs are disappearing, and there is nothing you can do about it. But from a technology perspective, there is a lot you can do. Digital innovations are re-inventing just about every field, creating exciting opportunities for those with the right skills.

As shown in the figure, we emphasize the importance of *double-deep* learning. By 'double-deep' we mean that individuals need the traditional skills in their field – sales, customer service, engineering, accounting, and so on – but they also need the technology skills relevant to that field. They don't have to be data scientists or programmers; they just need to know how to use and apply modern technologies.

Marketing is a good example. For traditional *single-deep* marketing people (who know mostly about, for example, live focus groups, mail surveys, promotional collateral, and print-based advertising) job prospects can be tough. But for double-deep marketeers (who know about search engine optimization, social media campaigns, internet ad placement, and similar digital services) the opportunities are many.

We believe this double-deep pattern holds true in just about every field – including IT professionals, who need more business and application knowledge. To be promotable (and even to remain employable) these skills must be continually enhanced. The required learning and attitudes are the main topics of Chapter 9. We will see that some individuals are dealing with these challenges much more directly than others.

Governments ask: What do these changes mean for our society?

**Tech giants,
start-ups, VCs**

**Self-sufficiency,
mass production**

**Software, data, and
analytic services**

**Rules and rights,
advanced usage**

**Robots, automation,
care for the aging**

**Skills, hacking,
dark web**

In recent years, many citizens around the world have become globalization skeptics. Workers in the West have seen wages stagnate and manufacturing move offshore, while many developing nations have seen their progress stall. Today's huge increases in economic inequality are undeniable.

The IT industry can't separate itself from these concerns, as technology has enabled globalization and has also been a major driver of inequality. This has left many governments in a quandary about how to best serve their people. Should they embrace global technology forces and the English-speaking internet, or should they resist these trends with more of a national sovereignty agenda?

Similarly, China, India, Russia, the European Union, Japan, and other nations have deep concerns about the long-running dominance of US IT firms. As suggested by the figure, the world's most powerful nations have different strengths and strategies, but they all want their share of the trillion-dollar technology marketplaces to come. In Chapter 11, we will assess this high-stakes global competition, with a particular focus on the inevitable battle between the US and China.

Chapter 11 will also show that smaller nations can have significant advantages in building advanced and cohesive digital societies. Israel, the Nordic/Baltic nations, Singapore, New Zealand, and others are demonstrating this in areas such as wireless bandwidth, citizen identity, online voting, digital currencies, smart grids, electronic healthcare and genealogical records, shared ledgers, and many others. The digital future won't just belong to the giants.

An increasingly intelligent digital 'Matrix' underlies these questions

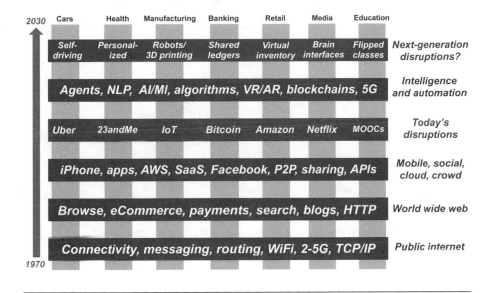

2030	Cars	Health	Manufacturing	Banking	Retail	Media	Education	
	Self-driving	Personal-ized	Robots/ 3D printing	Shared ledgers	Virtual inventory	Brain interfaces	Flipped classes	Next-generation disruptions?
	Agents, NLP, AI/MI, algorithms, VR/AR, blockchains, 5G							Intelligence and automation
	Uber	23andMe	IoT	Bitcoin	Amazon	Netflix	MOOCs	Today's disruptions
	iPhone, apps, AWS, SaaS, Facebook, P2P, sharing, APIs							Mobile, social, cloud, crowd
	Browse, eCommerce, payments, search, blogs, HTTP							World wide web
	Connectivity, messaging, routing, WiFi, 2-5G, TCP/IP							Public internet
1970								

Underlying all five of these questions is the emergence of the increasingly intelligent societal infrastructure that we have labeled *the Matrix*. Why choose a new word? What's wrong with *the cloud*?

As we will see throughout this book, new terms emerge to capture new circumstances. The digital world that we envision is best described by words such as intelligent, autonomous, embedded, pervasive, aware, and self-healing. Does this sound like a cloud? Besides, IT language is always evolving – from an *internet* of computers, to a *web* of pages and links, to a *cloud* of computing services. Each of these terms lasted about a decade, before the industry center of innovation moved on, as it is doing today.

Of course, the word 'matrix' comes with many connotations – the 1999 movie, the rows-and-columns nature of matrix mathematics, and, as shown above in the internet, web, cloud, and intelligence/automation layers, the way powerful *horizontal* services now cut across traditional vertical industry *stacks*. As we will explore in Chapters 1 through 5, each of these references is relevant to the future we envision.

But whether the term 'the Matrix' catches on or not is not important. What matters is that the image above helps you see that much of what we know and do is being absorbed into a vast societal infrastructure. This book will assess what this emerging matrix of capabilities means to industries, organizations, and individuals, as we move into the *post-cloud* era of the 2020s.

This book helps you see the *triple transformation* – of industries, organizations, and careers

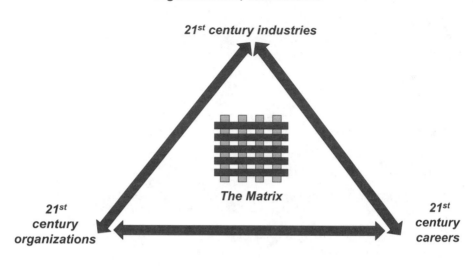

The figure above depicts the main focus of this book. How will industries, organizations, and careers be transformed in a Matrix-centric world? We will use a three-part structure:

In **Part 1**, we forecast the *post-cloud technology landscape*. Chapter 1 explains our concept of *the Matrix*, and how it is changing the way society innovates, operates, and competes. Chapter 2 explains why *machine intelligence* is advancing today, its current strengths and limitations, and why traditional firms are struggling to keep up.

Part 2 assesses the *triple transformation*. Chapter 3 describes the myths and realities of *industry disruption*. Chapter 4 discusses what firms mean when they say they want to become a *platform business*. Chapter 5 provides checklists to help firms leverage today's key *Matrix platforms*. Chapter 6 reviews the main risks associated with this more *outside-in* approach, with Chapter 7 arguing that *digital leadership* should be a team sport. Chapter 8 presents the important implications for the *Enterprise IT* function, while Chapter 9 summarizes the impact of these changes for individuals and careers, as innovation shifts to the *human platform*.

Part 3 examines the *strategic and global competitiveness* implications. Chapter 10 shows how companies can leverage *technology lifecycles* to better anticipate future market changes, while Chapter 11 examines *global IT industry* leadership, as the competition between the US and China intensifies.

We conclude with a reminder that *words matter*, and a summary of the key terminology we recommend for the 2020s.

Acknowledgements

Many LEF colleagues have contributed to this book, which is why it is written in the voice of 'we' (not that we always agree). However, any errors are entirely mine. Special thanks go to:

Douglas Neal and John Taylor for sensing how consumer technologies were taking over the IT landscape, and coining the term *consumerization*, way back in 2004

Alex Mayall, Robina Chatham, and the late Kirt Mead for their extensive and ongoing work into the Business/IT Relationship

Brinley Platts for his CIO Executive Profile models

Richard Sykes for his many insights into the Global Technology Services business

Mike Nelson for his research into Business Transparency in the age of WikiLeaks

Amir Hartman for his perspective on IT and the Board of Directors

Adrian Seccombe, Paul Dorey, and the late Jim Ginsburgh for identifying the *outside-in* nature of IT security architectures

Richard Bhanap for his expertise in the dynamics and politics of Digital Leadership

Professor Ed Hess of the Darden Business School for his work on Business Growth, and **Professor Ian Angell** of the London Business School for his insights into Business Uncertainty

Simon Wardley for his powerful *Wardley Map* frameworks, his ground-breaking research into China, and his vast knowledge of all things IT

Lewis Richards, Bob Barker, and Thomas Power for living their *21st Century Human* vision, and helping our clients experience the value of cutting-edge skills and technologies

Mark Zawacki for his insights into how Silicon Valley competes with its customers

Rob Atkinson and his team at the ITIF for their work on government technology policy

Dave Aron for keeping the LEF's research focused on a 21st century vision and mission

Glen Robinson and Bill Murray for bringing *the Matrix* into the heart of the traditional firm

James Gervers, Dave Reid, Ibrahim Jackson, Klaus Heinrich, Kathie Shannon, and Mohammed Khalid for connecting me with so many interesting organizations and individuals

Anne Pappenheim, Keren Hayden, Andy Scrivner, Ian Head, James Bodsworth, and Gareth Scragg for their invaluable editorial, production, graphics, publishing, technical, and marketing support

Jane Kingston, Kate Taylor, Melanie Shaw, and Sarah van der Burg for keeping me and the whole LEF ship afloat with such skill, wisdom, and good cheer

Lemuel Lasher for his long-term sponsorship, guidance, support, and intellectual engagement

Mike Lawrie (DXC CEO) **and Dan Hushon** (DXC CTO) for personally embracing our research, and making it part of what is now a 150,000-employee organization

Richard Davies (LEF Managing Director) for supporting my work no matter where it has led, including leveraging years' worth of valuable LEF IP to make this very unusual book possible

All of our DXC and Leading Edge Forum clients for their support, insight, and engagement

And finally, **Nicholas Negroponte**, whose 1995 internet classic, *Being Digital*, inspired the title of this work.

Part I

The Post-Cloud Technology Landscape

Chapter 1

From *the cloud* to *the Matrix*

In this chapter

- New words emerge to describe new realities
- The Matrix is changing how we innovate, operate, and compete
- Matrix innovation stems mostly from the consumer market
- A new layer of intelligence and automation is now being added
- Building out the Matrix is the biggest investment of our time
- New value creation is steadily migrating to the Matrix
- There will be intelligent Matrix services for just about everything
- Matrix firms typically play by very different rules
- Every industry has many intriguing Matrix/MI players
- Every country is seeking to get its own Matrix 'right'
- The Matrix will be the foundation of the 21st century economy
- How much does all this mean to you?

In this opening chapter, we will explain why we believe we are entering a post-cloud era. The technology environment of the 2020s will be increasingly intelligent, aware, autonomous, and embedded – no longer a cloud of remote services but rather a pervasive Matrix of capabilities, mirroring the full range of human activities. This vast societal infrastructure is rapidly becoming the world's economic center of gravity, which every business must adapt to. While many readers will be familiar with some of the trends and dynamics presented in this chapter, they set the stage for just about everything that follows.

New words emerge to describe new realities

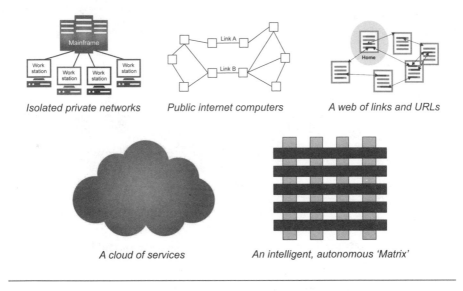

| *Isolated private networks* | *Public internet computers* | *A web of links and URLs* |

| *A cloud of services* | *An intelligent, autonomous 'Matrix'* |

Language evolves. While the terms *the internet*, *the web*, and *the cloud* are often used interchangeably, the emergence of each term coincided with a change in the digital landscape. As depicted in the figure above, new words coincided with new realities.

In this book, we will use 'the Matrix' to suggest that the focus of the IT industry is shifting once again – beyond today's paradigm of a 'cloud' of services 'out there,' to one where our individual lives, work, and things are deeply embedded in an ever-more intelligent and pervasive societal infrastructure.

Of course, the word 'Matrix' plays off the famous 1999 movie, with its machine dominance and virtual worlds. It also plays off the *rows* and *columns* nature of matrix mathematics, a fundamental machine-learning building block. But as we will explain on the next page, the thatched matrix image above is mostly designed to show how powerful horizontal services now cut across every traditional vertical industry stack.

Whether readers adopt the term 'Matrix' or not, the 2020s will have their own feel and focus[1]. Smart products, robots, wearables, implants, brain scans, blockchains, IoT, virtual and augmented reality, and many other innovations will expand digital innovation far beyond internet connectivity, web links, and cloud services. The Matrix will come to encompass most of what we do, and even how we see ourselves. We believe that the use of new terminology can help us see these changes more clearly.

---

1.   Other names considered included the Mesh, the Grid, the Metaverse, and the Digital Fabric.

The Matrix is changing how we innovate, operate, and compete

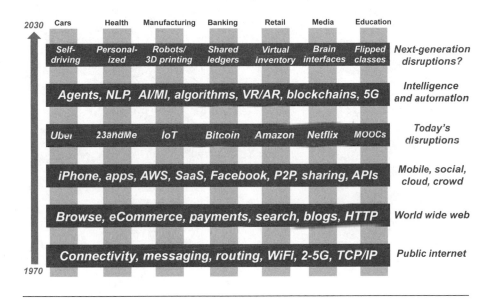

Just as roads, telephones, and electricity powered the 20th century economy, an intelligent digital infrastructure will underpin the societies of the 21st century. It's already changing how society innovates, operates, and competes.

As shown in the figure, our Matrix metaphor enables us to see this infrastructure in two important ways. First, there is a shift from mostly vertical to more horizontal business structures. During the 20th century, each major industry sector tended to have its own stack of processes, but 21st century firms increasingly rely on powerful *horizontal*, cross-industry capabilities. The major cross-industry companies – Google, Amazon, Facebook, Apple, and Microsoft – have become the most valuable firms in the world.

Second, these horizontal layers have built up through periodic waves of innovation: the initial public internet, the world wide web, the cloud/social/mobile era, and now a powerful new layer of machine intelligence and automation. Each previous layer created exciting new uses and disruptive new companies, and we expect this pattern to continue in the areas shown across the top of the figure, and more.

Incumbent firms will discover many opportunities if they can embrace these changes and develop effective Matrix strategies. But as the history of transportation and electrification suggests, major shifts in societal infrastructure often result in new industry leaders. Not every firm will make the transition to this post-cloud future.

Matrix innovation stems mostly from the consumer market

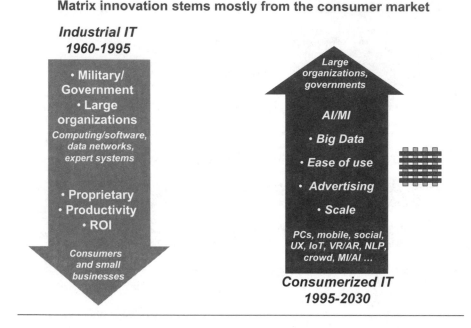

Taken literally, the film *The Matrix* presents a dystopian vision where humans are kept alive merely to provide the electricity that their machine overlords require. But taken metaphorically, the message isn't nearly so dark or far-fetched. Humans already power the IT industry through the things we buy, the advertising we consume, the content we upload, and the time we spend in the virtual world. As digital technology increasingly augments the human brain and body, as well as most of what we do and need, this metaphor will only strengthen.

As shown in the figure, Matrix innovation now increasingly comes from consumer markets and is *bottom-up* in terms of scale, funding, and operational practices. Companies such as Google, Facebook, Amazon, and Netflix have had to continually develop new technologies and methods to serve their billion-user marketplaces.

More intriguingly, and as we will explore in Chapter 2, our activity as consumers has generated the *Big Data* that has made many *deep learning* advances possible. For example, who would have guessed that millions of seemingly frivolous internet videos and photos of cats would play such an important role in developing today's impressive image recognition capabilities?

Looking ahead, today's consumer data volumes will eventually be surpassed by the data generated by hundreds of billions and someday trillions of machines and other internet-connected objects. Many of these devices will be edge-optimized – working offline, or connected only sporadically or locally – further strengthening our Matrix, post-cloud metaphor.

A new layer of intelligence and automation is now being added

1993-2005 –
Web/eCommerce

- Free media
- Browse/search
- Choice/convenience
- Aggregation
- Disintermediation
- Retail/payments

2006-2016 –
Social/mobile/cloud

- Mobility/apps/location
- Cloud computing
- Software-as-a-Service
- Social media/P2P
- Open source/sharing

2017-2030 –
Intelligence and automation

1. Deep learning algorithms
2. Speech/image processing
3. Software agents/bots
4. Blockchain ledgers
5. Smart contracts, digital cash
6. IoT, sensors, serverless
7. Vehicles, drones, robots, 5G
8. Smart products/systems
9. Wearables/implants, AR/VR
10. Biometrics/neuro-imaging

The key message of the figure above is that the Matrix is being built over time and in distinct phases. Although we have already enjoyed many wonderful digital applications and innovations, we expect that the technologies of the 2020s listed on the right of the figure will prove to be even more powerful, as they appear to enable even more fundamental and intelligent possibilities.

Of course, it is easy to be skeptical. Software agents still make amusing errors; virtual reality systems are still uncomfortable and dorky-looking; blockchain-based shared ledgers face complex implementation challenges; smart light switches and toothbrushes can make the internet of things (IoT) seem trivial; algorithms can have worrisome built-in biases; Bitcoin prices are mostly based on speculation and Bitcoins themselves are often used by criminals; and so on. There are many uncertainties ahead.

But skepticism has been part of every IT era. After the collapse of the dot.com bubble in the early 2000s, many compared the internet boom to the Dutch tulip craze of the early 1600s, only to watch the tech survivors soar to historic heights. Similarly, after Facebook's initial public offering got off to a shaky start, many dismissed the power of social media and the sharing economy. Events soon proved otherwise.

Given that the last two generations of skeptics have wound up decisively on the wrong side of history, we should be wary of betting on the third.

Building out the Matrix is the biggest investment of our time

	$ billion market cap				$ billion market cap
1. **Apple**	880		16. Chevron		238
2. **Alphabet (Google)**	735		17. Procter & Gamble		234
3. **Microsoft**	661	*Matrix firms*	18. Home Depot		222
4. **Amazon**	572	*have surged*	19. Pfizer		217
5. **Facebook**	519	*past the*	20. **Verizon**		**217**
6. Berkshire Hathaway	492	*banks, the oil*	21. **Intel**		**215**
7. Johnson & Johnson	378	*companies,*	22. Citigroup		198
8. JPMorgan Chase	372	*and everyone*	23. Coca-Cola		195
9. ExxonMobil	355	*else in terms*	24. **Cisco**		**190**
10. Bank of America	309	*of market*	25. **Comcast**		**188**
11. Wells Fargo	300	*capitalization*	26. PepsiCo		169
12. Walmart	294	*(12/31/17)*	27. Philip Morris		162
13. **Visa**	260		28. Disney		162
14. **Oracle**	240		29. Merck		153
15. **AT&T**	240		30. GE		150

The figure above shows the financial scale of the Matrix, which is the biggest economic initiative of our time. Stock market values will always be volatile, but Matrix companies now account for more than half of the total market capitalization of America's leading firms. While the numbers won't be quite as dramatic in other developed nations (due to the global dominance of US firms), information technology is as important to the 21st century economy as cars, fossil fuels, and financial services were to the 20th.

But even bigger infrastructure investments clearly lie ahead. Handling future data volumes will require much faster computers and two-way communications bandwidth, as we are still in the early stages of our use of sensors, smart products, autonomous vehicles, personalized medicine, the IoT, and other data-hungry technologies. Many experts believe that Moore's Law will run its course within a decade, making exotic (and expensive) technologies such as quantum computing increasingly necessary. High-speed wireless 5G networks will require another major build-out.

These technologies present daunting challenges in system design, complexity, command, control, integration, maintenance, power consumption, security, and self-healing operations. Every piece of the Matrix will require sustained innovation and investment for many years, and there are thousands of such pieces. While the overall process will take another decade or more, firms aligned with this vast utility build-out are very well positioned. Today's Matrix entrepreneurs should be viewed as the Edisons and (Nikola) Teslas of our time.

New value creation is steadily migrating to the Matrix

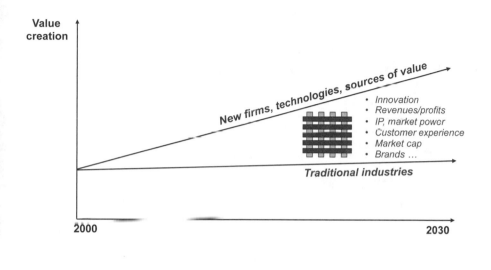

Value and profit migration have long been characteristics of changing technology marketplaces. For example, as the personal computer market grew in the 1980s and 90s, value and power shifted away from the system hardware vendors to specific value chain layers, especially the microprocessor (Intel) and the operating system (Microsoft). More recently, taxi industry market power has migrated decisively away from licensed taxi drivers to the previously weak dispatching service.

Today's wave of Matrix innovation will result in value migration across just about every sector. Consider how automobile value is now migrating to software and advanced mobile services; how healthcare value is migrating to edge devices, medical images, and other data sets; how advertising dollars have migrated to social and other digital media; how consumer buying criteria has migrated to online ratings; and, more worrisome, how military power is migrating to the cyber world and autonomous fighting systems.

The risk for incumbents is that although value migration tends to be cumulative, it is often barely perceptible to companies and employees who may feel they are doing just fine. But over time, these migrations result in a very different world. We encourage every organization to try to understand how value is migrating to the Matrix in their sector, and how they can take advantage of these changes. These issues will be covered much more deeply in Chapters 4 and 5, with their focus on leveraging specific Matrix *platforms* and capabilities.

There will be intelligent *Matrix services* for just about everything

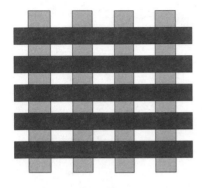

See, talk, listen, read, write, recognize, identify, translate, buy, sell, pay, auction, compute, store, back-up, locate, encrypt, share, search, collaborate, aggregate, rate, recommend, promote, advertise, instruct, advise, train, predict, forecast, repair, track, monitor, notify, measure, sense, analyze, control, optimize, comply, customize, arbitrate, design, create, entertain, and continually learn and improve ...

Looking ahead, it's safe to assume that IT suppliers will try to build a low-cost, often free Matrix service for just about everything that humans do. Capabilities such as talking, listening, recognizing faces, and translating languages will become as commonplace as identifying a song with Shazam or Googling a search term – both of which are actually complex machine intelligence (MI) activities. As MI experts have long observed, once a new application becomes ubiquitous, people no longer see it as MI; it's just another useful technology service.

Virtually every capability shown in the figure has the potential to be used by billions of people, and thus may someday be worth billions of dollars. These massive scale economies help us understand why, for example, in 2016 Microsoft paid some $300 million for SwiftKey, a tiny UK keystroke anticipation firm. Every little piece of the Matrix can be extremely valuable, and there are thousands of such pieces. This realization fuels much of today's venture capital industry.

Importantly, these services are designed to interact easily with one another, through either web services protocols and application programming interfaces (APIs), or services such as Zapier and IFTTT. In this sense, all of the services in the figure above can be seen as the building blocks of future *higher-order systems*, with capabilities we can barely imagine today. Think of how Uber pulled together existing smartphones, GPS mapping, payment APIs, and cloud servers to re-invent the taxi service industry.

Matrix firms typically play by very different rules

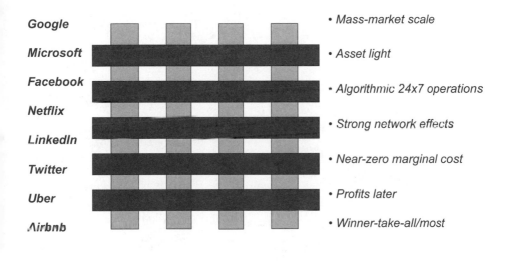

Google

Microsoft

Facebook

Netflix

LinkedIn

Twitter

Uber

Airbnb

- Mass-market scale
- Asset light
- Algorithmic 24x7 operations
- Strong network effects
- Near-zero marginal cost
- Profits later
- Winner-take-all/most

The reason that Matrix firms are potentially so disruptive is that they typically play by the very different rules listed in the figure above. Taken together, these traits have created some of the most successful business models ever developed.

For example, Matrix firms are often *asset* (and *balance-sheet*) *light* – Uber owns no vehicles, Airbnb no hotel rooms, Google and Facebook no content, and so on. Their costs are variable, and their *marginal cost effectively zero*. They readily adopt the latest practices and technologies, so continuous deployment (DevOps) is the norm. Their use of web standards enables agile, loosely coupled, and scalable services.

This core grounding in the cloud makes it relatively easy for these firms to ride up the machine learning curve – from real-time data acquisition to advanced analytics, algorithm development, personalization, and intelligent customer experiences, all leading to ever-more automated and self-aware operations.

But the biggest differences are still financial. Because of their strong *network effects* and scale economies, internet markets tend to be *winner-take-all*, with most of the profits going to a single market leader. Additionally, many Matrix firms have the luxury of taking a *profits later* approach. Consider Amazon, which for most of its history operated with little or no profit, enabling it to put relentless pressure on once-mighty Walmart. For better or worse, there are different financial rules for different generations of players, to an extent that to incumbents often feels 'unfair.'

Every industry has many intriguing Matrix/MI players

CarTech	FinTech	MedTech	LegalTech	EdTech
Uber	PayPal	Watson	Casetext	Coursera
Lyft	Apple	iHealth	Judicata	FutureLearn
Tesla	Kickstarter	WebMD	eBrevia	edX
Google	Kiva	23andMe	Alt Legal	Khan
Apple	Amazon	Fitbit	LegalZoom	Udacity
Zipcar	Square	Google	UpCounsel	AltSchool
Nvidia	Bitcoin	BioLert	Lawdingo	Knewton
Mobileye	Ethereum	Woebot	LawPal	YouTube
Didi Chuxing	Alipay	Chi-med	TianTong	TAL

The figure above lists some of the more prominent Matrix firms in selected industry sectors. Most industries have many such players, often referred to as *XTech* (as in *FinTech, CarTech, MedTech, EdTech,* and so on). While venture capitalists still prefer the larger potential market size of cross-industry businesses, the great success of Amazon, Uber, and Netflix has demonstrated the potential of sector-specific players (although it remains true that there are no comparable MedTech, EdTech, or LegalTech successes).

The figure lists both specialized start-ups and the major dot.com giants. Google, Apple, Facebook, and Amazon (sometimes collectively known as the *GAFA*) have almost unlimited financial resources, and thus no real bounds to their ambitions. But while these firms look unstoppable right now, tech's turbulent history suggests caution. Digital market leadership has always shifted significantly over time, and as we will see in Chapter 3, today's giants all face potentially disruptive future challenges. Innovative new firms are emerging all around the world.

At the bottom of each column is a major Chinese firm. Because China has nurtured its own Matrix companies, there is typically a direct Chinese counterpart to each of the major US giants – Amazon/Alibaba, Uber/Didi, Facebook/ Tencent, Google/Baidu, Apple/Huawei, and so on. While China has been successful in keeping the US leaders in check, the prospects for its firms outside of China remain uncertain. Nevertheless, other nations (especially India) have observed China's approach carefully, as ministers and local companies plan their country's digital future.

Every country is seeking to get its own Matrix 'right'

1. Modern, affordable infrastructure
2. Skilled and educated citizenry
3. Advanced universities and R&D
4. English language support/resistance
5. Smart cities, cashless society
6. Domestic company support
7. Start-ups and venture capital
8. Laws, regulations, taxation, antitrust
9. Dependency vs. self-sufficiency
10. Openness, privacy, censorship, standards

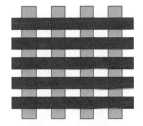

National Matrix strategies will be as diverse as the countries themselves

---

Just as each nation is responsible for its own roads, electricity grids, telephone systems, schools, and culture, so each country will shape its own Matrix in the areas listed above and more. The local digital economy is now a top priority in virtually every nation's domestic policy planning, with many governments appointing powerful digital ministers. There is already a great deal of local innovation and experimentation.

Many nations have understandably focused first on network quality and bandwidth, as this is an area they can control without much domestic controversy. China, Korea, Singapore, and Malaysia have been particularly aggressive in government-led infrastructure projects, in contrast with (for example) India, which started to modernize its national telecom system much later, and is now rushing to catch up by relying upon wireless technologies.

Political and cultural issues, while equally important, have proven more difficult to manage, as governments and their citizens often have sharply different views regarding issues such as social media usage and access to English-language content. As we will see in Chapter 11, we are drifting toward a less global, more multipolar Matrix, with national protectionism, censorship, and other controls often on the rise.

While there are no right or wrong answers regarding the optimal mix of public vs. private investment, open vs. closed systems, and global vs. local suppliers, recent events in many countries have shown how important technology decisions can be. Today, few things define a national culture more than its attitudes toward bandwidth, information, data, language, and speech.

The Matrix will be the foundation of the 21st century economy

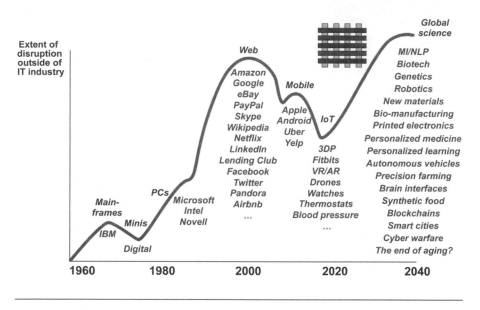

The figure above depicts our sense of the relative economic disruption caused by the major technology eras. Looking back, the disruptive impact of mainframes, minicomputers, and PCs seems relatively modest, with the biggest industry disruptions clearly coming from the initial dot.com boom. In contrast, although mobility has changed our lives in many important ways, with a few exceptions, it has been more of an additive than disruptive force. And as we will discuss in Chapter 3, the IoT is still in its early stages.

We are now entering the long Matrix rollout. Although no one knows exactly which industry incumbents or new digital players will prevail during this transition, there is less doubt about the post-cloud world that is emerging. Competition will drive the evolution of the Matrix to fill every conceivable market opportunity, as companies become more software-, data-, and algorithm-driven. This increasing *instrumentation* of society will enable important new levels of intelligence and automation.

Most importantly, the Matrix will become the foundation for the many global scientific advances we expect in the 2020s/30s. One doesn't have to fully embrace Ray Kurzweil's vision of *The Singularity*[2] to imagine that the innovations of today might soon seem primitive. The IT industry is only about 50 years old, and given the exponential way technology improves, the next 50 years will likely have significantly more impact. But whatever this wondrous technology-driven future is called, it's a safe bet that it won't be 'cloud.'

---

2. Ray Kurzweil, *The Singularity is Near*, Gerald Duckworth & Co Ltd, 2006

How much does all this mean to you?

1. Do you believe in this chapter's vision of an intelligent, Matrix-based society?

2. How is the Matrix changing how value is created in your field/industry?

3. How well do you track relevant new Matrix capabilities and developments?

4. Do you have the necessary skills and experience in these areas?

5. Is your nation building the intelligent digital infrastructure it needs?

6. Are you optimistic or fearful about where global science is taking us?

7. Are you more of a 'blue pill' or a 'red pill' person?

An entire digital universe is evolving outside of anyone's design or authority. While there may well be areas where you can shape the Matrix to your advantage, you can never control it. You can only adapt to it. The questions above can help you think about what this might mean to you.

Organizations need to acknowledge that the Matrix will become the foundation for much of the modern economy, and that this requires an *outside-in* perspective. This means looking to the external market first when thinking about how to innovate, operate, and compete in the future. The checklists provided in Chapter 5 can help firms see the range of these possibilities.

For individuals, the key question is how much technology matters to your career and future. While the answers will vary widely, people with digital skills are already enjoying substantial employment advantages. And as we will discuss in Chapter 9, these advantages will only grow as IT innovation shifts to the *human platform*.

For those companies and individuals who choose to engage with this world, the 2020s will present exciting opportunities. As Morpheus challenged Neo in the first Matrix film:

"There is no turning back. You take the blue pill – the story ends, you wake up in your bed and believe whatever you want to believe. You take the red pill – you stay in Wonderland, and I show you how deep the rabbit-hole goes."

Chapter 2

There is nothing artificial about machine intelligence (MI)

In this chapter

- We are just beginning to ask the big computing questions
- IT intelligence terminology is like a set of Russian dolls
- The Matrix is making *deep learning* possible
- There is now a formula for MI innovation
- But most traditional firms face a very different MI equation
- Can traditional firms close the MI gap?
- Focus on the MI uses of most relevance to you
- Plan for MI to be used across the full digital stack
- Think focused data sets, not writing code
- Expect bots for just about everything
- Choose the appropriate MI *operating model* for your firm
- We haven't reached an MI tipping point
- We may never solve the *black box* dilemma
- MI will eventually raise difficult ethical questions
- We should resist the big fears, at least for now

In this chapter, we will explain today's overall machine intelligence (MI) terminology, why the MI field is making such great progress today, its key forms and applications, the challenges it presents to traditional firms, and the need to focus on the very real forms of important new value MI enables, as opposed to today's almost entirely speculative fears.

We are just beginning to ask the big computing questions:

• How capable can we make systems and machines?

• Are there any limits to what can or should be done?

• How are human and machine intelligence different?

• How are they similar?

• How will they complement each other?

• How will they compete?

• Will human and machine capabilities increasingly merge?

• Will these technologies create a better, more prosperous world?

"This is the business we have chosen"

– The Godfather Part II

The questions above help us see why there is so much excitement about machine intelligence (MI) in the market today. While MI has long been the 'Holy Grail' of the computing community, these seminal questions are no longer just hypothetical.

Unfortunately, Western media tends to be much more drawn to the threats of technology than its virtues (consider *Frankenstein*, Hal in *2001*, and so on) and this is the case with MI today. Far more is said and written about MI's potential downsides – vanishing jobs, loss of control, diminished human worth – than the countless benefits of a much smarter world.

Oddly, these fears are even being raised by some prominent IT industry leaders. But while real risks may emerge in the very long run, today's laments remind us of a famous scene in *The Godfather Part II*. When Michael Corleone complains about the unexpected murders and reprisals his criminal organization has faced, Hyman Roth will have none of it, reminding Michael that "This is the business we have chosen."

For those of us in IT, the questions above define the business *we* have chosen. Competition will continue to push us forward, as will our deep-rooted human desire to discover what is possible. Besides, for the foreseeable future, the gains will far exceed the losses. There is no turning back, at least for now.

IT Intelligence terminology is like a set of Russian dolls

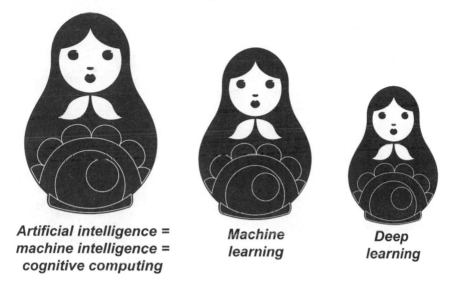

Artificial intelligence = machine intelligence = cognitive computing	Machine learning	Deep learning

Readers may have noticed that we use 'machine intelligence' rather than the more common term 'artificial intelligence.' As with the words 'cloud' and 'Matrix,' we do this because we think the right words can help us see things more clearly. The Russian Doll metaphor shown in the figure helps explain this.

In this view, *artificial intelligence (AI), machine intelligence (MI),* and *cognitive computing (CC)* are synonyms for the broad field of enabling computers to exhibit human-like capabilities. AI is the most widely used term today, while CC is used primarily by IBM and sometimes by Microsoft. However, we prefer MI because there is nothing *artificial* about computer intelligence, just as there is nothing artificial about the strength of a tractor. We think it's telling that while most people say "artificial intelligence," no one ever says "artificial learning." People used to say "artificial light" a lot, too.

In contrast, *machine learning (ML)* enables computers to become smarter *without explicit programming* – either with human support (supervised) or without (unsupervised). Thus, ML is a subset of the overall AI/MI field.

Finally, *deep learning (DL)* is a form of machine learning, with other forms including clustering, linear regressions, and Bayesian probabilities. While all of these approaches are still widely used, DL gets the most publicity because it has enabled rapid improvements in game playing, image processing, language translation, and other areas, as explained further on the next page.

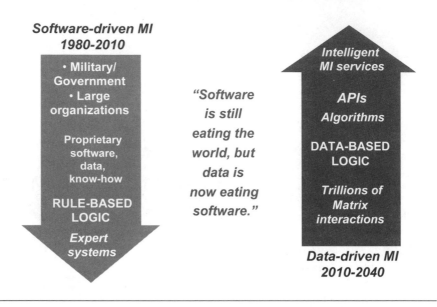

The Matrix is making *deep learning* possible

Software-driven MI 1980-2010

- Military/ Government
- Large organizations

Proprietary software, data, know-how

RULE-BASED LOGIC

Expert systems

"Software is still eating the world, but data is now eating software."

Intelligent MI services

APIs

Algorithms

DATA-BASED LOGIC

Trillions of Matrix interactions

Data-driven MI 2010-2040

One of the most widespread digital memes of recent years has been Netscape founder and now prominent venture capitalist Marc Andreessen's pronouncement that "software is eating the world[3]." By this he means that software has been steadily transforming every industry – from media to financial services to retail.

While this devouring continues, ideas evolve. Many tech insiders today like to say that yes, software is still eating the world, but data is now eating software. By this they mean that the traditional method of writing detailed procedural software is being challenged by a new approach in which machines are given an appropriate data set, and after a great deal of very complex mathematical analysis, the desired capabilities emerge. This is how deep learning works.

As shown in the figure, many of these data sets come from our use of the Matrix, and since more data enables better results, deep learning systems tend to improve naturally. It's a different and much more scalable dynamic than the long-standing (and still very important) expert system approach shown on the left side of the figure, where humans seek to encode their knowledge into fixed rules and decision trees.

While both methods will continue, deep learning has captured our imagination because it has enabled a broad range of impressive results, but also because it much more closely resembles the way the human brain works, as discussed later in this chapter.

---

3.   Marc Andreessen, *Why Software Is Eating The World*, Wall Street Journal, August 20, 2011

There is now a formula for MI innovation

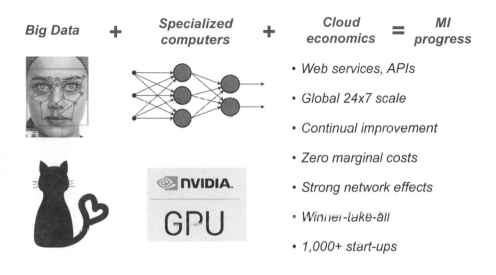

Big Data **+** *Specialized computers* **+** *Cloud economics* **=** *MI progress*

- *Web services, APIs*
- *Global 24x7 scale*
- *Continual improvement*
- *Zero marginal costs*
- *Strong network effects*
- *Winner-take-all*
- *1,000+ start-ups*

Deep learning does not exist in a vacuum; it is part of an overall formula for machine intelligence innovation. Today, there are three main components:

- **Big Data.** Facebook leads in facial recognition because it has the faces; Google leads in language translation because it has the best set of multi-lingual documents; computers can recognize even a silhouette image of a cat because there are so many cat images to learn from. Deep learning needs lots of data with which to train itself, and the Matrix companies tend to have the best data.

- **Specialized computers.** Deep learning systems require vast computing power. Fortunately, the major cloud providers (Amazon, Microsoft, Google) and semiconductor firms (Nvidia and others) have responded. A new cycle of specialized semiconductors is now underway, and may eventually lead to quantum computing. Processing power is still a significant MI bottleneck, but much less than it used to be.

- **Cloud economics.** While most MI work has historically taken place in universities, large corporations, and government agencies, the Matrix is now the target MI platform. As we have seen, every piece of the Matrix is a potential source of new wealth – motivating entrepreneurs, venture capitalists, and industry giants alike.

While we are still a long way from having general-purpose computer intelligence, this simple three-part formula will enable exciting advances on a great many MI fronts.

But most traditional firms face a very different MI equation

Islands of data	+	Limited MI skills	+	ROI economics	=	Widening gap
Data is locked in silos, client-specific, or otherwise not readily available at sufficient quality and scale		Skills in analytics and deep learning are scarce, and often don't fit well within entrenched operating models		Cloud pricing, delivery and service models are typically in sharp conflict with current incentives and financial requirements		Machine intelligence innovation will continue to be driven by the tech giants and specialized players

This is one of the biggest challenges that traditional firms face

---

What strikes us about this Matrix-based formula for MI innovation is how different it is from the situation in most traditional firms today.

Firms that already operate algorithmically – for logistics, reservations, credit scoring, price optimization, actuarial patterns, financial trading, and similar automated services – generally have a clear path forward. These businesses know what it means to be data-driven, and are used to automated decision-making. They can use deep learning to improve their algorithms.

But most large organizations are still struggling with Big Data, let alone machine learning. Their data tends to be kept within product, service, customer, or organizational silos, making effective aggregation difficult – sometimes even illegal. They also tend to have very limited access to advanced deep learning skills, and their general rate of MI hiring is relatively slow.

More troubling, their internal data often requires extensive cleaning and labeling in order to usefully capture specific domain knowledge. The work is hard; the costs are high; the skills are scarce; and the benefits often speculative. IBM and Watson have run up against these challenges in a number of high-profile accounts.

The business model conflict is equally problematic. Most traditional businesses find it hard to run on anything but return on investment (ROI) criteria. This is in sharp contrast to the Matrix giants who are willing to invest heavily in new areas and accept sustained losses. It's no wonder that new firms continue to lead in most MI areas.

Can traditional firms close the MI gap?

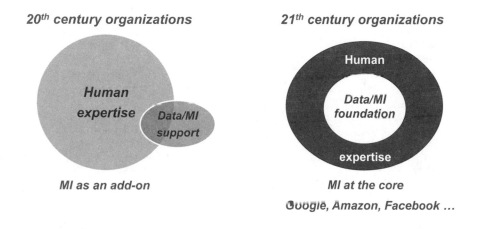

20*th* century organizations

Human expertise

Data/MI support

MI as an add-on

21*th* century organizations

Human

Data/MI foundation

expertise

MI at the core

Google, Amazon, Facebook ...

The widening gap between the way most traditional firms and today's internet giants operate is depicted in the important figure above. The difference is so great that it raises the question of whether every firm will eventually need to move toward this sort of data foundation model. Today, most companies are still skeptical. We often hear:

- "We don't make any money doing any of this stuff."
- "We're doing fine as is."
- "I'll be retired before any of this matters to our bottom line."
- "Maybe in the other industries, but not in ours."

The difficult thing about the first three of these statements is that they are often true, as building intelligent algorithmic operations will take time. The fourth claim is mostly wishful thinking, grounded in our tendency to see our own situations as more special than they really are. Taken together, they are a formula for "Let's wait and see."

Thus, building a 21st century data foundation in a world often full of more immediate pressures requires leaders who believe in an MI-driven future. Technology has proven the skeptics wrong time and again. Odds are, it will do so once more. The rest of this chapter will help traditional firms visualize how the current gap might stop widening and eventually begin to close.

Focus on the MI uses of most relevance to you

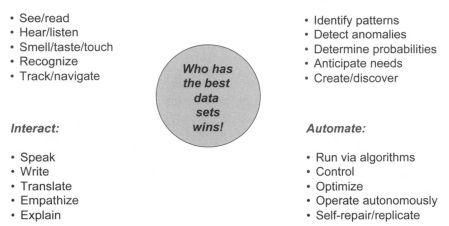

Sense:

- See/read
- Hear/listen
- Smell/taste/touch
- Recognize
- Track/navigate

Analyze:

- Identify patterns
- Detect anomalies
- Determine probabilities
- Anticipate needs
- Create/discover

Interact:

- Speak
- Write
- Translate
- Empathize
- Explain

Automate:

- Run via algorithms
- Control
- Optimize
- Operate autonomously
- Self-repair/replicate

As with human intelligence, there are multiple forms of machine intelligence. We have grouped twenty of the most important MI uses into the four categories shown above:

- **Sense.** The ability of machines to see, hear, smell, and recognize is improving steadily. Future systems will likely be able to accurately identify not just any person, but also (for example) every type of animal, plant, building, product, voice, image, activity, or design.
- **Interact.** Successful Natural Language Processing (NLP) would greatly reduce our reliance on keyboards and displays, enabling much more *ambient intelligence*. However, most of the NLP uses in the near term will be in specific application areas.
- **Analyze.** The distinction between Big Data analytics and MI is often more of degree than kind, as just about every large organization is now mining its data to some extent. The big difference today is the addition of deep learning to the data scientist's toolkit.
- **Automate.** While the fifteen uses in the first three groups above will often leverage open source algorithms and APIs, MI-based automation is typically a customized mix of sensing, interacting, and analyzing. For example, a self-driving car must recognize its surroundings, interact with people and objects, and analyze its options in real time.

Companies should assess which of these 20 areas are most important to them, and where the most useful data sets are emerging, with the understanding that whoever has the best data in a particular area will likely have important competitive advantages.

Plan for MI to be used across the full digital 'stack'

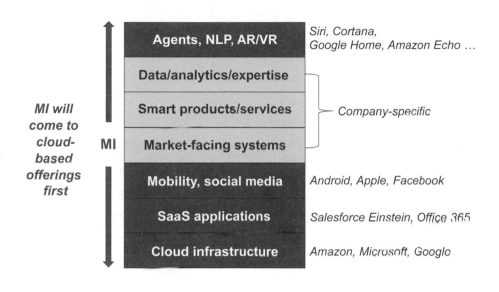

One of our earliest MI research findings a few years ago was that large organizations will *use* much more MI than they will *build.* As shown in the figure, the major technology suppliers intend to incorporate advanced machine learning into their offerings, and thus, these capabilities will be brought to their customers as a matter of course. For example:

- Amazon is integrating MI capabilities into every aspect of Amazon Web Services (AWS) to automate its operations. Microsoft and others are doing the same.
- Today, Salesforce's Einstein is the most visible example of adding MI to a mainstream application, but most future applications will be smart ones.
- Facebook will add all manner of image recognition, emotion analytics, and similar MI capabilities to its core services.
- Google, Microsoft, Apple, Amazon, Facebook, and others around the world are in an all-out battle to help firms build a natural language interface to their customers.

Taking advantage of these supply-side services will be much easier for firms that have embraced cloud computing and *Software-as-a-Service (SaaS)* offerings (as opposed to proprietary on-premises systems). It's another incentive to move to the cloud.

Importantly, in order to evolve toward an intelligent end-to-end digital stack, these supply-side MI services should be supplemented by internal MI efforts in areas such as market-facing systems, smart products, and associated analytics. Customers will eventually judge your firm by your capabilities in these front-of-the-firm areas.

Think focused data sets, not writing code

• *Games won/lost*	• *Digitized music*	• *Facial emotions*
• *Medical images*	• *Individual voices*	• *Reputation/behavior*
• *Maps/routes*	• *fMRIs for emotions*	• *Heartbeat patterns*
• *Facial images*	• *fMRIs for learning*	• *Strength/balance*
• *Eyeball images*	• *fMRIs for truth*	• *Breath/sleep patterns*
• *Gait patterns*	• *Satellite images*	• *Fitness, exercise*
• *Plant/animal images*	• *Traffic patterns*	• *Exam/essay grading*
• *Object images*	• *Telecom traffic*	• *Sentencing terms*
• *Style images*	• *Maintenance needs*	• *Recidivism rates*
• *Genetic profiles*	• *Crop data*	• *Actuarial patterns*
• *Translated language pairs*	• *Activity videos*	• *Quantitative self*

We are still a long way from having *generalized machine intelligence* (GMI), and many people in the MI field question whether today's bottom-up, deep learning processes can ever match the human ability to adapt to unexpected circumstances. They argue that top-down, knowledge representation capabilities will also be needed. Probably so.

But this limitation won't prevent the success of specific MI initiatives. Indeed, as we look at the MI landscape today, we see parallels with the app industry. As shown in the figure, there will be a wide range of focused deep learning applications, each revolving around its own data set, giving new meaning to the familiar notion of being *data-driven*.

It is logical to expect that some of these applications will have winner-take-all characteristics, as they will often have strong network effects – i.e. the more people that use them, the better they will get. But it is also likely that, like apps, other MI markets will be highly competitive, as different data sets are compiled and different algorithms tested. Some even argue that the data sets themselves can be bypassed, and that machine learning can sometimes be based entirely on simulations.

While these are all complex topics in markets that are still in their early years, the bottom line is that the lack of GMI will not stop important new MI value from being created.

Expect bots for just about everything

- *Information feeds*
- *Customer support*
- *Oversight/tracking*
- *Arrange meetings*
- *Email tone analysis*
- *Emergency services*
- *Photo editing tips*
- *Media recommendations*
- *Insurance claims*
- *Financial advice*
- *Statistical services*
- *Game-playing strategies*
- *Search engine interfaces*

- *Instructions/advice*
- *Grammar corrections*
- *Travel arrangements*
- *Logistics suggestions*
- *Scheduling updates*
- *Calling a cab*
- *Booking a table*
- *Dietary/calorie tips*
- *Warnings/detections*
- *Pricing alerts*
- *Behavioral nudges*
- *Psychotherapy*
- *Jokes, fun, facts*

Just as MI is naturally stemming out of the Matrix, so will bots sit on top of most future applications. The list of possibilities in the figure shows how useful it will be to have an agent-like front-end that can automate activities, provide notifications and emergency status updates, coordinate participants, and manage similar repeatable tasks. Although integrating bots with back-end systems is still difficult, it will eventually seem odd that earlier generations of applications lacked such built-in assistance. Bots are becoming an important form of applied MI.

Perhaps the most visible bot application today is setting up meetings. Systems such as Zoom.ai and x.ai automate the often-cumbersome task of finding workable meeting times across people's schedules. They also get us used to engaging with messages that we know are being written and sent entirely by machines, as shown below:

> Hi David, it is Ava again (Kathie Shannon's assistant).
> Your meeting with Kathie Shannon is now set on Thursday, July 27 from 1:30pm to 2:00pm at Skype Meeting.
> If you need to reschedule or cancel this meeting, just go back to https://zoom.ai/go/sw4Cgc
> Have a great day! – Ava Zoom
> Want your own assistant? Sign-up for free at www.zoom.ai!

While embracing this type of interaction is similar to how we had to get used to talking to voice response systems, it clearly moves us closer to a *Turing Test*[4] world.

---

4. A M Turing, 'Computing Machinery and Intelligence', *Mind*, October 1950

Choose the appropriate MI *operating model* for your firm

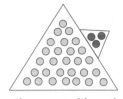

Autonomous activities   *Captive consulting shop*

Center of excellence   *Cockpit corporation*

Today, most companies are unsure of the best way to manage their MI talent and activities. We have observed four main approaches:

- **Autonomous activities.** The thinking here is that MI is relatively new, so business units should decide what makes sense in their respective areas. While decentralization has many advantages, it can also be inefficient.
- **Captive consulting shop.** Here, the idea is that a central group is the most efficient way to leverage scarce MI skills. Again, there are clear advantages, but there are also the risks of lack of accountability and isolation from actual business needs.
- **Centers of excellence (CoE).** This model has long been popular in areas such as mobility, apps, web site design, and so on. Skilled MI people can focus on specific business areas, while also being part of an active community.
- **Cockpit corporation.** Over time, many market leaders will embrace this model, where an advanced central group works closely with focused communities throughout their organization. It's pretty much today's Silicon Valley approach.

What about Enterprise IT? The IT organization could be an area of autonomous MI activity; it could be the captive consulting shop, or be part of a CoE community. It could even sit in the actual cockpit. Or it could be none of the above. The main thing is for companies to be clear about who is responsible for what.

We haven't reached an MI tipping point

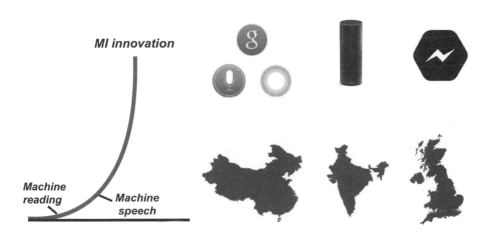

Despite all the legitimate excitement today, we can't stress enough that we have not yet reached a tipping point, even for focused MI applications. Hardware, bandwidth, and skill shortages, and data availability/quality remain significant gating factors.

But we are getting closer. The impressive success of Amazon's Alexa suggests that NLP is becoming a reality, at least in some specific domains and applications, and this has triggered all-out competition between Google, Amazon, Facebook, Apple, Microsoft, IBM, and others around the world. Although it is still early in the game, Amazon's sudden NLP leadership clearly caught the tech world by surprise.

We see NLP as a likely tipping point because it is the gateway to a post-smartphone, post-PC world. For example, imagine an Alexa-like product in hospital rooms so patients' voice commands could turn the lights/TV on or off, or find out when the next meal or doctor's visit will be. Similarly, educators imagine future systems being like having a 24x7 tutor. NLP will surely enable an entirely new generation of eyes- and hands-free applications.

A second and perhaps even greater tipping point might occur when machines are able to read and comprehend at adult levels, but at computer speeds. However, as the figure indicates, machine reading significantly lags machine speech, although Alibaba and Microsoft have recently shown real progress in various machine reading tests.

We may never solve the *black box* dilemma

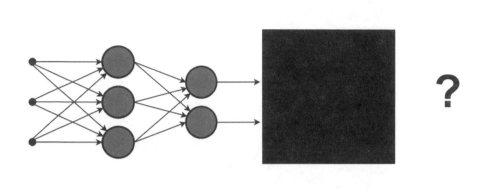

Whether a deep learning system is playing Go, interpreting an X-ray or identifying an object, people often ask how the system decided what it did. On the surface, this seems a reasonable request. After all, humans are often asked to explain their reasoning, so why shouldn't machines? Indeed, many regulatory processes in healthcare, insurance, and other industries require this degree of transparency.

However, as shown in the figure, most deep learning systems today are essentially 'black boxes' whose output can be accepted or rejected, but not easily explained. Whether this situation will change is an ongoing debate within the MI field, and one where the majority of experts seems to believe that the black box model is here to stay.

The reality is that the human brain also has many black box traits. For example, try to explain in words how you can be 100 percent sure when you see a dog. It's pretty much impossible, yet based on years of experience (data), you just 'know.' Indeed, experts in many fields report knowing things they can't fully explain, and in this sense, human and machine intelligence may not be as different as we sometimes think.

While MI developers will seek to improve *explainability* through weighting, visualization, and other techniques (see IBM's WatsonPaths), the need to accept black box-based decisions will have important implications for the nature of 21st century digital trust, assurance, and auditability. This is discussed further on the following page.

MI will eventually raise difficult ethical questions

Comfort	Discomfort	Creepiness
• Navigating	• Diagnosing	• Flying
• Teaching	• Investing	• Driving
• Ride sharing	• Grading	• Policing
• Translating	• Litigating	• Fighting
• Dating	• Auditing	• Brain interfaces
• Reporting	• Watching	• Implants
• Entertaining	• Psychoanalyzing	• Genetic design

Turning human tasks over to machines is not just a matter of technology. People must be comfortable with these changes, and this often comes down to trust and assurance.

As suggested by the three columns in the figure, overcoming the *creepiness* and *Big Brother* factors will be easier in some areas than others. But it is worth keeping in mind that not long ago, many of us were uncomfortable accepting dates over the internet, renting a spare bedroom to a stranger, or getting into an unmarked, privately-owned car instead of a taxi. Societal attitudes can change quickly.

Today, the middle column appears particularly interesting because it covers *the professions* – doctors, lawyers, professors, accountants, and so on. As these fields tend to face common challenges in high costs, affordable citizen access, and heavy workloads, MI-based automation seems especially needed, as will be discussed in Chapter 3.

But the high-risk categories shown on the right of the figure are beyond what most of us are currently ready to embrace – especially anything to do with policing and warfare. However, not only can people's views change quickly, but perspectives can vary widely around the world. What is deemed unacceptable in one country might be seen as a necessity or a competitive advantage in another. We expect that many of these high-risk thresholds will be crossed in the coming years.

We should resist the big fears, at least for now

- Massive job losses aren't occurring

- We've been dependent upon machines for a long time

- Losing at Go and chess hasn't changed our sense of human worth

- Science has always been a black box to most people

- Digital addiction looks a lot like TV addiction

- New technologies almost always increase economic inequality, initially

- Algorithms tend to have fewer biases than humans

- Technology increases privacy, not just reduces it

The benefits of MI are many and real, while the dangers, although certainly possible, are almost entirely speculative at this time

---

While there have always been societal fears that computers would eventually lead to human diminishment and even obsolescence, these concerns are now being expressed more regularly and more urgently than ever, even by some of the leading technologists of our time, such as Elon Musk. These warnings tend to fall into three main categories:

- **Economic impact.** There is much discussion (and a number of influential studies) of the likely extent of job losses due to machine automation, as well as MI's increasing effects on economic inequality, and the subsequent need for a 'guaranteed income.'

- **Diminished human worth.** If machines turn out to be better than humans at just about everything, how will this affect our sense of ourselves?

- **Ethics.** There is much debate about algorithmic biases and manipulation, fake news, Big Brother-style surveillance, how driverless cars and robots should behave in particular no-win situations, and similar controversies.

History says that these worries will prove to be exaggerated, and as itemized in the figure above, this has been the case thus far. In the near term, the benefits of MI – particularly the combination of human and machine intelligence – will be considerable and real, while the downsides will remain almost entirely speculative. However, we certainly can't rule out the possibility that this balance might shift over time, and thus the overall MI debate will surely continue.

Part II
The Digital Transformation Journey

Chapter 3

The myths and realities of industry disruption

In this chapter

- Within the IT industry, disruptions are the norm
- Digital disruptions tend to follow a common pattern
- Myth #1: Technology is changing society as never before
- Myth #2: The pace of technology change is accelerating
- Reality #1: Every industry has at least one big disruptive scenario
- Reality #2: "Software is eating the world"
- Reality #3: Silicon Valley has a *dual disruption* agenda
- Reality #4: The barriers to disruption are often substantial
- Reality #5: Actual industry disruption varies widely
- Electric/self-driving cars could have the most economic impact
- Robotics and 3D printing could have the most global trade impact
- Cyber warfare could have the most political impact
- Disrupting *the professions* would have the most symbolic impact
- Healthcare disruption is the most needed
- Educational changes could face the most resistance
- Blockchains could have the most financial services impact
- Even the GAFA are not immune

In this chapter, we will discuss the history of IT industry disruption, the typical pattern of disruptive industry change, some common misperceptions regarding both the term 'disruptive innovation' and the pace of technology adoption, the state of industry disruption today, and the extent to which the Matrix, MI, and related technologies will transform a wide range of currently undisrupted industry sectors.

Within the IT industry, disruptions are the norm

Mainframes	Minis	PCs	Mobile	Internet
IBM	Digital	IBM	Apple	Google
Sperry	IBM	Microsoft	Google	Amazon
Burroughs	Data General	Intel	Samsung	Facebook
Honeywell	Wang	Apple	Huawei	eBay
NCR	Prime	HP	Xiaomi	Twitter
CDC	HP	Dell	ARM	LinkedIn
ICL	Sun	Seagate	HTC	PayPal
Amdahl	Tandem	Compaq	RIM	Netflix
Siemens	Oracle	Sony	Motorola	Uber
Fujitsu	Bull	Toshiba	Palm	Airbnb
Hitachi	Olivetti	Amstrad	Nokia	Didi Chuxing
Cray	NEC	Lenovo	Ericsson	Baidu

1970 ■■■■■■■■■■■■■■■■■■■■■■■■■■■■➔ 2020

The pattern in the figure above is clear. Each major phase of IT innovation has been led by a new generation of firms. Although a few companies have succeeded in multiple IT eras, ambitious entrepreneurs who could see where the market was going have consistently defeated firms whose success was based on where the market has been. While in everyday English, the word 'disruption' can be used to describe anything that shakes up the status quo, in the digital world, it mostly refers to this unusual market leadership pattern.

The figure also highlights two other important dynamics. First, while the IT industry has always had strong market leaders – especially IBM, Microsoft, and Intel – this tendency has become even more pronounced during the internet era, to the point where all of the firms listed in the right-hand column above enjoy near winner-take-all status. This extraordinary combination of new-generational leadership and near-monopoly industry structures explains the strong interest in disruptive innovation in recent years. People want to know if these highly lucrative patterns will continue with the technologies of the 2020s.

The second important dynamic is the dominance of US firms over the 50 years shown. Here again the key question is whether this pattern will continue. Thus far, China has proved to be the only nation that has created strong across-the-board rivals to the US giants – as strategists in Europe, India, and elsewhere have surely noticed.

Digital disruptions tend to follow a common pattern

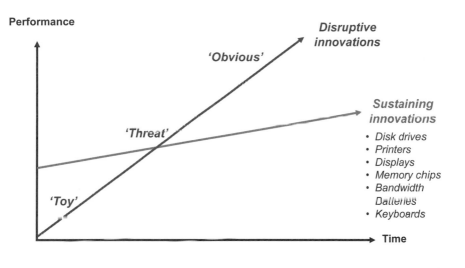

Many of the now-defunct companies shown on the previous page had first-rate technologists who understood where the digital world was headed. So why couldn't they adapt to a changing marketplace? Clayton Christensen has long been the most influential business professor within the technology industry because he so effectively answered this question[5].

Christensen's key insight was that truly disruptive innovations conflict so fundamentally with the core customer needs, business practices, and financial incentives of incumbent firms that it is actually in their short-term interest to resist the new approach. They develop an almost allergic reaction to the innovation.

We have simplified Christensen's thinking in the figure above. When a new technology emerges, it is often immature and easily seen as a 'toy' that can be safely ignored – even ridiculed. But as the technology improves, it becomes an increasingly serious 'threat' to be actively resisted. In the final stage, the new technology becomes the 'obvious' new order. But by then it is too late. There are many such 'toys' today – Bitcoins, 3D printing, smart watches, IoT healthcare devices, Alexa, VR headsets, and so on.

But importantly, not all innovations are disruptive; indeed, most aren't. Christensen distinguishes between *disruptive* and *sustaining* innovations: the latter fit well into incumbent business models, while the former do not. Unfortunately, this essential distinction is often lost in the business press today, resulting in an exaggerated sense of disruptive change – as evidenced by the two big myths that follow.

5. Clayton M Christensen, *The Innovator's Dilemma: When New Technologies Cause Great Firms to Fail*, Harvard Business School Press, 1997

Myth #1: Technology is changing society as never before

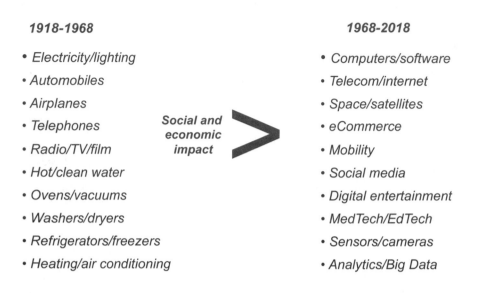

1918-1968	1968-2018
• Electricity/lighting	• Computers/software
• Automobiles	• Telecom/internet
• Airplanes	• Space/satellites
• Telephones	• eCommerce
• Radio/TV/film	• Mobility
• Hot/clean water	• Social media
• Ovens/vacuums	• Digital entertainment
• Washers/dryers	• MedTech/EdTech
• Refrigerators/freezers	• Sensors/cameras
• Heating/air conditioning	• Analytics/Big Data

Social and economic impact >

We often hear that we live in uniquely disruptive times. But as shown above, the first half of the 20th century was also a remarkable period, featuring many important innovations. In comparing the two eras, we think it is indisputable that the last 50 years of information technology innovation have not come close to matching either the societal or economic impact of the 50 years before.

We don't say this to disparage the advances of our times, but simply to add some historical perspective. Consider which were the bigger societal changes: telephony to Skype, or telegrams to telephony? Cars to self-driving cars, or horses to cars? Aircraft to drones, or ground to air transportation? Passive grids to smart grids, or the electrical grid itself? As endlessly fascinating as the web is today, radio, television, movies, and recorded music had at least as much revolutionary impact on our information and entertainment habits as Facebook, Twitter, Netflix, Spotify, and YouTube.

But of course, we are still very early in the game. As discussed in Chapters 1, 2, and 9, the next 50 years may well see advances that make today's economy seem primitive, as the work of the global science community steadily re-invents virtually every industry and field. The sheer range of possibilities ensures that industry disruption will remain an important topic for many years to come.

Myth #2: The pace of technology change is accelerating

	Date first commercialized	Used in 50% of US homes	Elapsed years
Electricity	1900	1930	30
Telephones	1910	1946	36
Radios	1922	1931	9
Televisions	1946	1954	8
Personal computers	1977	1993	16
World wide web	1993/1989	2002	9/13
Mobile phones	1983	1995	12
eBooks/tablets	2004	2013	9
Home robots (Roomba)	2002	?	
Fitbits and similar	2007	?	
Consumer 3D printers	2010	?	How many of these devices
Smart watches	2010	?	will reach the 50%
DIY blood pressure	2011	?	threshold
Smart thermostats	2011	?	In less than
Consumer drones	2013	?	10 years?
VR, 3D goggles	2015	?	

A second claim that we often hear is that we live in a period of accelerating technology change. However, the data mostly indicates otherwise.

The time it takes for a new technology to be adopted by 50 percent of US households is a useful standard for cross-technology comparisons. While the historical data is often sketchy, it appears that both radios (9 years) and black-and-white televisions (8) reached the 50 percent threshold much faster than personal computers (16) or mobile (not just smart) phones (12). Technologies – such as electricity and telephones – that required massive new physical infrastructure have understandably taken longer[6].

Even more indisputably, today's early *internet of things* (IoT) offerings – Roombas, Fitbits, smart watches, IoT thermostats, AR/VR, etc. – are clearly being adopted comparatively slowly, a dynamic that is not sufficiently acknowledged.

So why do we have this sense of accelerating change? Mostly, it's the vast scale, presence, and wealth of today's tech giants. But it's important to realize that Google, Facebook, and Amazon have been able to ride on top of the existing internet, and in this sense they are analogous to television and radio networks, which grew rapidly by sitting on top of the electrical grid. The bottom line is that the global use of the internet has exploded, even as the adoption of new *devices* is often slower than in earlier times.

With these definitional, historical, and myth-busting perspectives as background, let's look at the realities of digital disruption today.

---

6. Electricity, telephone, radio, and television data drawn from *Historical Statistics of the United States, Colonial Times to 1970*, US Department of Commerce, 1975

Reality #1: Every industry has at least one big disruptive scenario

1. Will large retail stores mostly disappear?

2. Will driving/owning your own car become the exception, not the rule?

3. Will traditional banks lose control over the global payment system?

4. Will robots and 3D printing reverse today's offshore manufacturing advantages?

5. Will machines make better diagnoses than doctors?

6. Will alternative energies replace the fossil fuel industry?

7. Will MOOCs eliminate many 2nd and 3rd tier colleges?

8. Will virtual reality make HDTV yesterday's entertainment?

Do you really want to bet against these changes?

9. Will fMRI and biometrics establish the legal *truth?*

10. Will cyber warfare be the future of military power?

For each of the questions listed in the figure above, the issue is essentially the same. The potential of modern technology to fundamentally alter the existing market order is staring right at us. We recommend that readers pause and ponder these questions, and imagine what the world might look like in the not-too-distant future. As a rule, we think it is unwise to bet against most of these changes over the long run.

What remains to be seen is how quickly things will change, whether traditional industry leaders will hold their positions, whether new firms will grow into future industry giants, and what level of incumbent/start-up co-existence will or won't prevail. While it may take a decade for the answers to many of these questions to be fully evident, history teaches us that the early movers have significant – although certainly not always decisive – advantages.

Additionally, it is important to keep in mind that disruption is rarely total. There are still plenty of traditional printed books and newspapers, travel agents, retail stores, hotels, taxi services, packaged software products, and even CDs and vinyl record sales. Thus in many industries, disruption is less a matter of outright replacement and more one of the *value migration* discussed in Chapter 1, as profits and market power move toward new digital and software-based approaches, as discussed further on the next page.

Reality #2: "Software is eating the world"

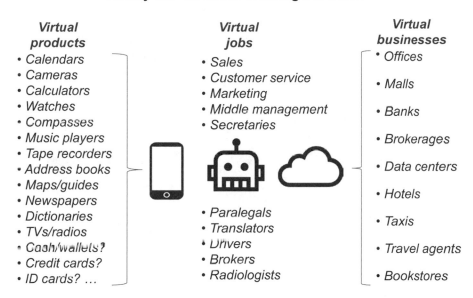

Virtual products	Virtual jobs	Virtual businesses
• Calendars	• Sales	• Offices
• Cameras	• Customer service	• Malls
• Calculators	• Marketing	
• Watches	• Middle management	• Banks
• Compasses	• Secretaries	
• Music players		• Brokerages
• Tape recorders		
• Address books		• Data centers
• Maps/guides		
• Newspapers		• Hotels
• Dictionaries	• Paralegals	• Taxis
• TVs/radios	• Translators	
• Cash/wallets?	• Drivers	• Travel agents
• Credit cards?	• Brokers	
• ID cards? ...	• Radiologists	• Bookstores

As we noted in Chapter 2, software has been devouring the world since the early days of the web. In all of the uses above, the software-based version is either free or less expensive than the physical world approach, and often functionally better as well. Smartphones provide the most obvious examples – just look at how many physical products we no longer need, with the virtualization of cash, wallets, credit cards, and various forms of identification almost certain to follow. The environmental benefits of this virtualization have been substantial, and generally under-appreciated.

Software's ability to virtualize jobs is, of course, a much more sensitive subject. But while all of the jobs listed above have been significantly affected by technology, thus far there has been more augmentation than outright replacement. As long as this remains the case, this issue should be politically manageable, although it will surely stay in the spotlight. We will take a closer look at technology's impact on employment in Chapters 9 and 11.

Lastly, technology is also virtualizing many physical facilities, especially those listed above. By far the biggest disruptions have been in retail, where many stores have closed, mostly because of Amazon. Indeed, entire malls are now being shut down, and others re-imagined as essentially indoor cities with housing, restaurants, entertainment, gardens, escape from the heat or cold, and even schools, government offices, and religious services. The long-term societal effects will likely be profound.

Reality #3: Silicon Valley has a *dual disruption* agenda

Technology disruptions	*Industry-specific disruptions*

Technology disruptions

- Cloud, SaaS
- Mobility, apps
- Social, P2P
- Open source
- Big Data, analytics
- Sensors, wearables, IoT
- Speech, facial recognition
- AR/VR/3D/AI/MI

Industry-specific disruptions

- Cars – shared, electric, self-driving
- Banking – advice, lending, Bitcoin
- Health – self-service, diagnoses, IoT
- Insurance – personalized, algorithmic
- Manufacturing – robotics, 3D printing
- Retail – Amazon, no inventory, China
- Education – MOOCs, flipped classes
- Legal – smart contracts, digital truth

Silicon Valley (broadly defined) has long been the high-tech capital of the world. Since the 1970s, it has been developing a technology stack that serves as the central nervous system of companies globally. It dominates the market for computers, applications software, networking equipment, database technology, storage, operating systems, and all manner of semiconductors.

'The Valley' expects this dominance to continue through the technologies listed on the left side of the figure and more. Indeed, rightly or wrongly, this success is now largely taken for granted, and the big question in the Valley today is whether its dominance can be extended to the industry-specific opportunities on the right side of the figure. This is what we mean when we say that Silicon Valley now has a dual disruption agenda.

This expanded agenda means that Silicon Valley is no longer just supplying tools and services. In many cases it is competing directly with the very companies it is supplying. Amazon is particularly aggressive here, competing against the core businesses of companies who are simultaneously major customers of its Amazon Web Services. (In contrast, Microsoft and IBM regularly reassure their customers that they won't compete with them, and for Microsoft especially, this is an important differentiator.)

Taken together, the Silicon Valley giants and literally thousands of start-ups clearly have enormous disruptive potential, cutting across every industry sector. But as we will see, they often face significant barriers.

Reality #4: The barriers to disruption are often substantial

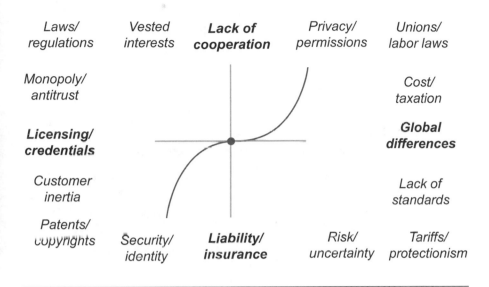

| Laws/ regulations | Vested interests | **Lack of cooperation** | Privacy/ permissions | Unions/ labor laws |

Monopoly/ antitrust · Cost/ taxation

Licensing/ credentials · **Global differences**

Customer inertia · Lack of standards

| Patents/ copyrights | Security/ identity | **Liability/ insurance** | Risk/ uncertainty | Tariffs/ protectionism |

As suggested by the figure, disruptive innovations eventually reach an inflection point, where the course of a market decisively shifts. However, many barriers can get in the way. While all of the challenges listed above can slow the rate of change, below we highlight four of the most significant:

- **Licensing/credentials.** Should you need a government license to be an Uber driver, an Airbnb provider, or an online teacher/trainer? Such decisions are being made all around the world, sometimes in the disruptor's favor, sometimes not.
- **Insurance/liability.** In areas such as driverless cars, IoT-based healthcare and digital cash, product liabilities are often unclear, and thus new forms of customer assurance are required. But until such services are available, reaching critical mass is difficult.
- **Lack of cooperation.** Competitors often don't work well with one another, for both strategic and antitrust reasons, but blockchains, self-driving cars, IoT security, and other future areas will require extensive industry cooperation.
- **Global differences.** Disruptive change would be accelerated by globally consistent practices, but many of today's non-disrupted sectors (including banking, insurance, health, and education) remain mostly national in nature.

However, these barriers can also create a false sense of comfort. While start-ups see barriers as nuisances to be ignored first and managed later, incumbents typically want clarity before moving aggressively. Thus the barriers that seem to protect incumbents often leave the risk-taking to others, and this can become its own disruptive dynamic.

Reality #5: Actual industry disruption varies widely

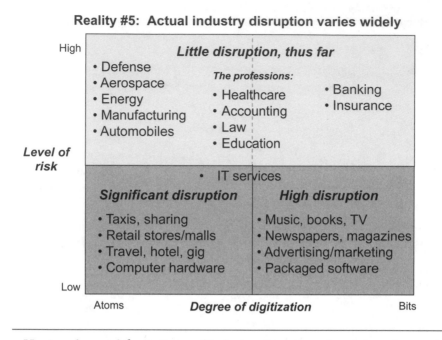

Having observed the patterns of industry disruption since internet usage took off in 1995, we have long used the 2x2 framework above. The x-axis shows to what extent the products of an industry are physical (*atoms*) as opposed to digital (*bits*). The y-axis compares the relative risk (security, liability, regulatory) profile faced by that industry. The professional sectors – healthcare, law, accounting, education, IT – have significant bits (information) and atoms (human delivery) dimensions.

It is important to understand that the placement of each industry in the figure is not based on whether that industry has been disrupted or not. Each industry's position is determined entirely by its atom/bits and risk profile. However, plotting each sector in this way reveals the overall pattern of change.

The lower right quadrant (low security, digital businesses) has been by far the most disrupted sector, followed by the lower left quadrant (low security, physical businesses). This suggests that bit-based businesses tend to change faster than atom-based ones.

More importantly, the industries in the upper half of the figure have experienced far less change, suggesting that the level of risk has thus far been the dominant disruptive determinant. So the key disruption question going forward is simply *what will happen in these higher-risk sectors?* Over the rest of this chapter, we'll assess the outlook for these industries. We'll see that while the overall picture is mixed, every industry has an intriguing disruption story.

Electric/self-driving cars could have the most economic impact

Levels of autonomous car operation*	Affected sectors
Level 0 – *No self-driving features*	• **Auto components**
Level 1 – *Limited driver assistance*	• **Oil/gasoline/energy**
	• **Gas stations**
Level 2 – *Multiple, integrated assistance*	• **Repair services**
Level 3 – *Limited, temporary autonomy*	• **Parking lots**
Level 4 – *Autonomous with human oversight*	• **Pipelines/fuel trucks**
	• **Drivers/deliveries**
Level 5 – *Autonomous operation only*	• **Insurance ...**

*from The Society of Automotive Engineers

The automobile industry (broadly defined) dominated the 20th century economy. But today, many young people have little interest in owning a car, and a significant number don't even learn to drive. City dwellers especially can often save time and money by not maintaining, insuring, and parking an automobile. But while ride-sharing services will continue to thrive (less than 1 percent of US car journeys are now ride share) and will reduce the total number of cars otherwise needed, they won't disrupt the auto-making industry itself.

Similarly, electric cars will likely disrupt many of the ancillary sectors listed above, but not necessarily the actual vehicle makers. Both hybrid and electric-only cars seem poised to grow quickly, due to improved batteries, environmental pressures, and government subsidies, but most car incumbents seem capable of managing this transition.

Self-driving cars would challenge the auto makers more fundamentally. However, while there will be successful usage in specialized applications, we don't expect mass-market autonomous vehicles until the 2030s. Today, we are just getting past Level 1 and into Levels 2 and 3. Fully autonomous Level 5 cars – which wouldn't need steering wheels, foot pedals, and so on – could well be led by new entrants, but it's far too early to say. While Silicon Valley is currently ahead of Detroit, Japan, Germany, and Korea, this could easily change, especially as many global alliances are likely. China and India are wild cards, especially in any Level 5 scenarios.

Robotics and 3D printing could have the most global trade impact

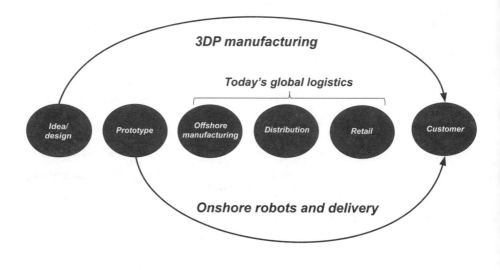

Mass manufacturing has long relied on low labor costs and vast global distribution systems, a business model that has fueled the rise of Japan, Taiwan, Korea, and (most recently and dramatically) China. As suggested by the figure, we see two main ways by which this model might shift from the *moving of goods* to the *moving of information*:

- **Robots.** Robots are enabling some work to come back onshore, as Asia's labor costs rise, energy prices fall, political pressures mount, and robots improve. However, the overall global trade impact has been modest. China uses robots, and *cobots* (robots that collaborate with humans), too.

- **3D printers.** The leading uses here have been for prototypes, custom parts, advanced designs, new materials and prosthetics, as well as in remote areas such as battlefields, submarines, and spaceships. As there is currently little use of 3D printing for mass-produced goods, 3DP is more complementary than disruptive.

Smart products are sometimes suggested as a third disruptive possibility, the thinking being that such goods should be made closer to where they are designed. However, in most such markets, offshore manufacturing quickly becomes the norm once products reach their high-volume phase, and China is already an innovator in many smart product marketplaces.

Thus, Asia should continue to lead global manufacturing through the 2020s, as China's position seems certain to strengthen further. If anything is to fundamentally disrupt this scenario, it will likely be political, trade, and/or military disputes.

Cyber warfare could have the most political impact

Critical infrastructures are vulnerable

1. Banking, trading, and payment systems
2. Electrical grids and power plants
3. Ground and mobile telecom networks
4. Space, satellite, and GPS systems
5. Ground and air traffic control systems
6. Dams, canals, and water systems
7. Hospitals and healthcare systems
8. Voting and registration systems
9. Military and government systems
10. The internet itself

Future wars could

be won without

firing a shot, and

be waged by

non-state actors

Defense has long been among the most stable of industry sectors, characterized by high stakes but relatively cozy competition between a small number of large defense contractors, with essentially one major buyer per country and one market leader (the US).

But the signs of change are everywhere today. The skills needed to operate a drone are similar to those in consumer video games. Robots and miniaturization will create entirely new and controversial ways of fighting. America's traditional dominance of space and satellite-based systems will be challenged. Non-state actors and asymmetric dynamics will not go away. China and Russia will continue to invest heavily in new technology-based capabilities.

However, as shown in the figure, perhaps the biggest question is whether virtual warfare will rival or exceed traditional military power. Should one nation be able to control or disable the critical infrastructures of another, there might be little need for armed conflict – and the long list of systems upon which society now depends shows how vulnerable we could be. All of the major powers are seeking to shore up these systems, but many key systems may already have been compromised.

While the ethics of cyber warfare remain controversial, the need to keep up with rivals creates pressure to explore any and all potential advantages, and unfortunately this makes future cyber conflicts – at least limited ones – likely. Overall, national defenses appear to have multiple paths to disruption in the not-too-distant future.

Disrupting *the professions* would have the most symbolic impact

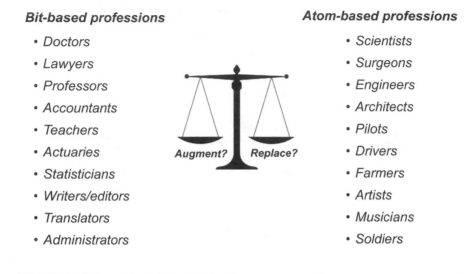

Bit-based professions	Atom-based professions

- *Doctors*
- *Lawyers*
- *Professors*
- *Accountants*
- *Teachers*
- *Actuaries*
- *Statisticians*
- *Writers/editors*
- *Translators*
- *Administrators*

Augment?   *Replace?*

- *Scientists*
- *Surgeons*
- *Engineers*
- *Architects*
- *Pilots*
- *Drivers*
- *Farmers*
- *Artists*
- *Musicians*
- *Soldiers*

Few areas of disruption would have more cultural impact than the professions. The roles shown above represent many of the highest forms of human learning. Will machine intelligence mostly augment these capabilities, or replace them? It's a bellwether issue.

Clearly, professional *augmentation* will be widespread and substantial in areas such as information access, decision trees, 24x7 availability, literature review, language translation, correspondence, billings, personalization, quality assurance, objectivity, warnings, detection, costs, training, reporting, and compliance. In the areas on the right of the figure, cobots will open up powerful new possibilities.

Although professional *replacement* has been modest so far, the technologies of the 2020s – deep learning, expert systems, software agents, blockchains, smart contracts, neuro-imaging, and robo advice – are aimed directly at knowledge, learning, and trust; the very traits that have defined the professions for centuries. These technologies also appear to be the only viable way to alleviate today's widespread cost and citizen access pressures, and in this sense large-scale professional disruption is often what society needs.

The potential for change is clearly there. Imagine Amazon selling prescription drugs, or insisting on shared ledger accounting across its supply chain; Facebook gathering together everyone with a particular medical condition; Google re-inventing language learning through its speech and translation services; or the use of brain neuro-imaging to legally prove someone is telling the truth. Expect the disruption of the professions to accelerate throughout the 2020s, as discussed further on the next several pages.

Healthcare disruption is the most needed

1. **Image analysis** – Cheaper, more accurate, consistent, global, 24x7

2. **Expert systems** – For diagnoses, treatments, side effects, interactions, discovery

3. **Self-service** – DIY tests, treatments, monitoring, retail, in-home services

4. **Patient experience** – Efficacy, satisfaction, ratings/reviews, transparency, trust

5. **Personalization** – Genetics, treatments, incentives, behavioral nudges

6. **Disease tracking** – Real-time patterns for epidemics, vaccinations, early warnings

7. **Aggregated data** – Family histories, societal records, 23andMe, personal profiles

8. **Language translation** – In admissions, emergency rooms, hospital rooms, 24x7

9. **R&D** – For discovery, sensory augmentation, implants, prosthetics, robotics

10. **Authentication** – Identity, privacy, anonymity, tamper resistance

---

In most developed nations, the healthcare industry faces similar challenges: rising costs, insufficient citizen access, over-burdened staff, uneven quality, and an often-unsatisfying consumer experience. Many medical professionals believe that machine intelligence and automation is the only viable way to relieve these pressures.

While the pace of change is still relatively slow, we believe that healthcare industry value is migrating to the Matrix right now in all of the areas listed above and more. Today, the delivery of medical services mostly revolves around hospitals and their associated medical megaplexes, in what is essentially an inside-out model, where the customer is expected to travel to the supplier.

We expect this model to de-massify over time, so that visiting the hospital will become the last resort rather than the first. Diagnostic, treatment, and supporting services will become more virtual, algorithmic, retail, do-it-yourself, and networked, as telematics and the sharing/gig economies are integrated into the healthcare ecosystem. Over time, hospitals will need substantially fewer beds, as services move closer to the patients and as people increasingly remain in their own homes for treatment.

By pulling work (such as blood tests, reading medical images, and processing customer records) out of physical, local institutions, service providers can achieve important scale economies, centralize expertise, and build the focused data sets needed for machine learning. Over time, we expect the healthcare industry to rely on a powerful set of external platforms, as we will explain further in Chapter 4.

Educational changes could face the most resistance

1. **Flipped classes** – Watch lectures at home, do homework in the classroom

2. **MOOCs** – Lower costs, global markets, star professors

3. **Personalization** – Self-paced learning based on interests, aptitudes, needs

4. **Automated grading** – Of essays, language proficiency, etc.

5. **Writing analysis** – Grammar, syntax, vocabulary, training, improvement

6. **Speech** – Recognition/synthesis, for language learning, visually impaired

7. **Teacher analytics** – Detect biases, errors; analyze trends, patterns

8. **Translation** – For language learning, multi-lingual content, real-time, 24x7

9. **Brain patterns** – For diagnostics, assistance, attention patterns, motivation

10. **Accreditation** – For college equivalency, micro degrees, hiring confidence

---

Whether we are looking at the doctor/patient, attorney/client, or teacher/student relationship, it's clear that 'the professions' are not just another business. The fact that the word 'customer' is so rarely used reflects an asymmetric culture. We think this dynamic is at its strongest in education, as students are at a more impressionable age.

Technology has yet to significantly alter this situation. In fact, the history of technology in the classroom is mostly one of continual disappointment – with radio, television, audio recordings, film, VCRs, personal computers, and CD-ROMs all once highly touted, with remarkably little to show for them.

And yet the efforts continue, especially in the areas shown in the figure. Once again, the potential is clear. Wouldn't it be great to combine speech recognition with language translation, and learn a language by talking to an intelligent software agent? Doesn't it make sense to watch a world-class teacher at home, and then do homework in the classroom under a local teacher's guidance? Wouldn't grading, testing, and credentials be more objective and consistent if done in a more standardized way?

While it's hard to argue against the vision of specialized educational services being deployed at scale, history suggests caution. Although we continue to be interested in the future of Massive Open Online Courses (MOOCs), their impact on university education has been modest. Given government, academic, and societal inertia, disrupting the education industry may prove to be the hardest challenge of all.

Blockchains could have the most financial services impact

Key blockchain applications

1. Shared ledgers
2. Digital cash
3. Smart contracts
4. Money transfers
5. Initial coin offerings
6. Settlements/clearance
7. Proof of ownership
8. Asset tracking
9. Supply chain integrity
10. Individual identities

As we noted in Chapter 1, the Matrix is not just enabling new digital services, but adding important new layers of digital automation and trust. With its built-in *encryption, proof of work,* and *immutability,* blockchain technology is now at the heart of many such efforts. Proponents see blockchain-enabled shared ledgers as the most important accounting innovation since double-entry bookkeeping back in the 1500s.

But today, the skeptics still have the upper hand. While there are many blockchain pilot projects, there are few large-scale deployments outside of Bitcoin itself. It's not just that blockchain technologies are highly complex; it's that shared ledger systems often require close and sustained cooperation between multiple parties, and this can be difficult when a system cuts across entrenched sectors such as accounting, banking, insurance, auditing, government, software, and law, as many blockchains do.

Nevertheless, given the compelling applications shown in the figure, we think shared ledger systems will thrive in the 2020s, often with disruptive results. Governments want to eliminate paper cash, and people want to send money globally as freely as they send email. We are particularly interested in *initial coin offerings* (ICOs) as a way of monetizing open source and other projects. Eventually, there will also be a widespread need for smart, self-executing, micropayment contracts. Thus far, the banking, accounting, legal, and insurance industries have largely brushed off the FinTech and LegalTech challenges, but the big Matrix players have yet to make their move(s).

Even the GAFA are not immune

- **G**oogle makes most of its money via search and related advertising, but what if future searches are sent or received via non-Google voice agents, from within Facebook or via a major *semantic* breakthrough?

- **A**pple is the world's most profitable firm because it can price its products far above their production costs. But how long can this be sustained if the differences between IOS and Android devices diminish over time?

- **F**acebook makes its money from its users' time and content. But what if Facebook-like capabilities could be offered via an open source, *Facebook-without-Facebook* P2P model, where users are directly compensated for their time and content?

- **A**mazon has invested massively in automated warehouse systems, but what if product searches could be linked directly to delivery/logistics systems so that no central inventory is actually needed?

Remember, IBM and Microsoft were once seen as invincible, too, with the exact same antitrust pressures and concerns as the GAFA face today

---

The giants of the IT industry look unstoppable today. They have unlimited cash, the world's top digital talent, farsighted leaders, powerful global brands, and seemingly boundless ambitions. Self-driving cars? Space travel? Internet dirigibles? Intelligent agents? Virtual reality movies? Brain implants? Live to 150? Why not?

But it was ever thus. IBM was going to use satellites to bypass the telecom industry, and would set up its own bank; Microsoft had similar satellite ambitions for Teledesic, and would become a media colossus. While both firms set off antitrust alarms in the US and Europe, these fears soon proved to be exaggerated. Both IBM and Microsoft largely missed the internet revolution – although today's rejuvenated Microsoft is once again a vital industry force.

As shown above, similar future disruptions are certainly possible. Today's giants tend to be vulnerable to more open, peer-to-peer business models, and the wider sharing economy. Like IBM and Microsoft in the past, they too are now facing growing antitrust and other regulatory pressures. The general public is becoming increasingly skeptical.

While major shifts are far from inevitable, today's giants are more vulnerable than previous industry leaders in at least one way: the customer switching costs are mostly ones of changing habits, not conversion effort and cost, and this relative ease of transition could be an important factor sometime down the road. Expect at least one of today's Matrix giants to eventually prove to be more fragile than we currently think.

Chapter 4
Becoming a platform organization

In this chapter

- Large corporations seek the optimal level of business integration
- Optimizing global integration is usually even more challenging
- Technology and organizations are merging into 'platforms'
- Traditional organizations are seeking to *re-platform* their business
- The computer industry runs on layers of 'horizontal' platforms
- Digital platforms bypass the traditional *value discipline* trade-offs
- A digital platform IS the customer and/or user experience (CX/UX)
- Digital platforms require team-based development approaches
- *Co-creation* platforms harness the crowd and the customer
- Expect important new co-creation platforms to steadily emerge
- Industry structures tend to run in cycles – the automobile example
- Which models will underpin the technology platforms of the 2020s?
- An expanding range of business paradigms – 1970-2030

In this chapter, we will explain why the term 'platform' has become so popular in business today. For decades, the computer industry has been grounded in a platform-based approach, with one technology innovation built upon another to enable continual improvement and evolution. But now that traditional businesses must increasingly become 'digital first,' platform thinking – and its associated designs and economics – is reshaping industry and organizational strategies in just about every business sector. In many ways, the Matrix can be seen as a vast web of interlocking platforms.

Large corporations seek the optimal level of business integration

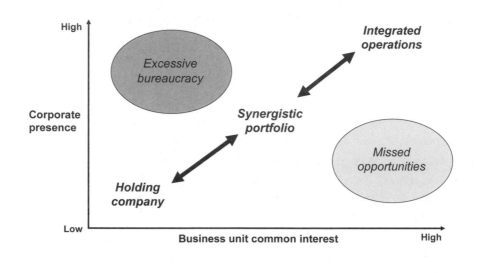

Once businesses grow and start to expand into new areas, they typically face some basic organizational questions. Do they want to be mostly centralized or decentralized? Should business units be synergistic or independently accountable?

Optimal company structures fall somewhere along the diagonal line shown in the figure. Too much corporate presence, and the firm will become overly bureaucratized; too little, and synergies and/or efficiencies can easily be lost. Diversified multinational firms have sought such optimization since their earliest days.

But although the challenge isn't new, this model still reveals a lot about the technology industry today. For example, when Google set up its Alphabet holding company in 2015, it was acknowledging that while there are strong synergies between its search, email, and YouTube businesses, the company's efforts in (for example) Nest appliances, self-driving cars, and life sciences are much less synergistic. In contrast, Apple continually seeks to leverage the many hardware and software synergies across its Macs, smartphones, tablets, and watches.

Perhaps the most interesting situation today is Amazon's. As a company, Amazon seeks to disrupt existing industries, and thus it often competes directly with traditional firms, most of which are also major customers of Amazon's AWS cloud computing unit. This underlying conflict of interest has often led to speculation that AWS may eventually become a more independent entity. We'll see. Amazon, like every company, must think through its optimal operating model approach.

Optimizing global integration is usually even more challenging

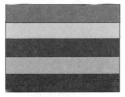

Strong countries

Regional operations

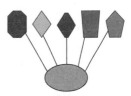

Separate divisions

Global product lines

Highly matrixed

Platform-based?

These centralization/decentralization decisions get more complicated as companies expand globally. For example, even if business units have relatively little in common, does it really make sense for every country to set up its own sales, marketing, and administrative systems?

Such dilemmas have challenged multinational firms for as long as they have existed, with the responses evolving steadily over the years. For example, before modern computing and telecommunications, large corporations often had very strong single-country operations, with country managers very powerful and living large. But as markets globalized and competition intensified, many firms opted for more streamlined regional and/or global product line strategies, seeking to sell the same product in the same way all around the world, significantly reducing local autonomy.

More recently, the need to leverage local capabilities, comply with local regulations, and be perceived as good local citizens has led many firms to set up substantial operations in many countries, relying on complex *matrix management* structures. This approach has been further strengthened by the rise of China, India, and other large national markets where robust country operations are once again seen as the best way to address unique local characteristics.

Not surprisingly, the resulting multinational structures have become highly complex. In response, many companies are now asking if *digital platforms* can bypass these challenges and provide the synergy, simplicity, collaboration, and responsiveness they seek. As expanded upon in this chapter, this seems the most likely path forward.

Technology and organizations are merging into 'platforms'

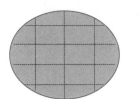

Integrated solutions

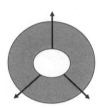

Digital platforms

"Platform:

a raised, level

surface on which

people or things

can stand."

Oxford English Dictionary

Focused specialists

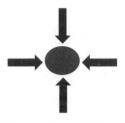

Co-creation platforms

For over a century, business thinkers have speculated about the structure of industries and the subsequent 'nature of the firm.' During the pre-internet era, two models dominated: vertical (linear) integration and horizontal specialization. The former is optimized for an integrated customer solution, say an IBM mainframe or an Apple Mac, where the hardware, software, and support all come from one firm; as opposed to the latter, where for example in Windows PCs, the microprocessors, disk drives, software, and displays come from specialized suppliers, optimizing *innovation, scale,* and *efficiency.*

Today's digital platforms challenge both of these models in two main ways. First, as we shall see, digital platforms, like today's Matrix leaders, can be optimized for integrated solutions and specialized efficiency at the same time, long thought to be impossible. More pointedly, as companies seek to become *digital first*, their technology platform and its underlying support organization can render the firm's geographic structures increasingly subordinate – a potentially fundamental shift in organizational thinking.

In recent years, powerful *co-creation platforms* (also called *n-sided markets*) have also emerged. Consider that the value provided by (for example) Facebook, Uber, Airbnb, and LinkedIn comes primarily from the people using the service. We will show that this model, where the customer is the *means of production*, will be critical to the future of machine intelligence, open communities, blockchains, and the human platform.

Today, all four of the models above can be viewed as 'platforms.' Our outlook for each is assessed over the rest of this chapter.

Traditional organizations are seeking to *re-platform* their business

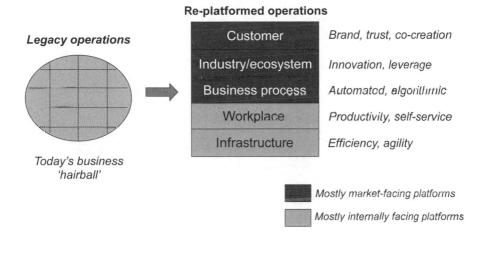

Re-platformed operations

Legacy operations		
Customer	Brand, trust, co-creation
Industry/ecosystem	Innovation, leverage
Business process	Automatcd, algorilhmic
Workplace	Productivity, self-service
Infrastructure	Efficiency, agility

Today's business
'hairball'

■ Mostly market-facing platforms
▢ Mostly internally facing platforms

Within the corporate world today, the use of the word 'platform' has sharply increased. As always, the emergence of new language is telling us something. But what? We have distilled two main messages.

Most obviously, today's Matrix giants are often described as platforms, and who wouldn't want to be more like them? Thus, when traditional firms say they want to become *platform organizations*, they are subtly borrowing the tech leaders' cachet, while also implying that they want to become a similar *go-to* place for leadership and innovation within their ecosystem.

From a more internal perspective, traditional companies are often a dense 'hairball' of complexity, with many overlapping systems, applications, and security processes. Here, the desire for digital platforms – and *re-platforming* – is really a call for simplicity and a more intuitive, Amazon-like user experience. Again, who wouldn't want this?

Both motives are built into the figure above. Internally, Enterprise IT seeks to provide efficient self-service infrastructure and workplace platforms. Externally, business units and senior leadership want more robust, software-defined processes, as well as the ability to shape the industry and customer platforms of the future.

Taken together, becoming a 'go-to' place for innovation, providing a simplified customer experience, and becoming a true digital-first organization is a pretty good working definition of what most traditional firms mean by 'digital transformation'. But while these words are easy to say, the technical and cultural challenges are often formidable.

The computer industry runs on layers of 'horizontal' platforms

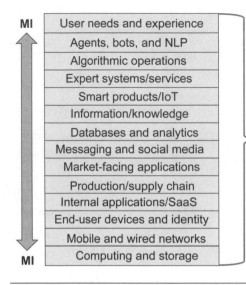

MI

| User needs and experience |
| Agents, bots, and NLP |
| Algorithmic operations |
| Expert systems/services |
| Smart products/IoT |
| Information/knowledge |
| Databases and analytics |
| Messaging and social media |
| Market-facing applications |
| Production/supply chain |
| Internal applications/SaaS |
| End-user devices and identity |
| Mobile and wired networks |
| Computing and storage |

MI

The modern 'digital stack' consists of countless nested and often invisible functional layers, each of which can be viewed as a 'platform,' upon which other platforms can stand. In this way, virtually every technology company can be seen as a 'platform organization.'

Inside the IT industry, the word 'platform' has long been used to describe just about any technology product or service that others can build on top of, including microprocessors, PCs, operating systems, servers, databases, software applications, web sites, eCommerce systems, smartphones, apps, social media services, IoT devices, application programming interfaces, intranets, wikis, collaboration software, open source code repositories, smart watches, VR/AR headsets, and more.

It's actually hard to think of an IT product or service that isn't designed to work or operate as a platform in one way or another. As suggested by the figure above, modern computer systems consist of layered and interoperable stacks of often-invisible capabilities, with each layer being constantly improved, commoditized or re-invented. This specialized, layered thinking has been built into the very heart of internet/web/cloud/Matrix designs and evolution.

In this sense, platform mindsets, designs, and architectures are more naturally aligned with horizontal IT industry structures than more vertically integrated traditional approaches, and this explains why many IT suppliers intuitively see themselves as platforms, while traditional firms feel the need to undergo complex transformation and re-platforming initiatives.

In short, technology firms have always used the word 'platform' because that's who they are and how they operate. Pre-digital firms have adopted the word 'platform' because that's what they hope to become. Taken together, platform thinking is now both the language and the design model of the modern digital marketplace.

Digital platforms bypass the traditional *value discipline* trade-offs

While specialization has always been an important business dynamic, digital specialization can be quite different from the specialization in (for example) the automobile industry, where every aspect of the modern car – tires, batteries, radios, fuel, services – is its own competitive marketplace.

This difference is depicted in the figure above. In 1995, Michael Treacy and Fred Wiersema argued that companies could excel in one of three areas – *product leadership (PL), operational efficiency (OE),* or *customer intimacy (CI)*[7]. Strategically, they needed to choose which discipline to focus on, and then be competitive in the other two.

This thinking made great sense in the pre-digital age – with Sony (PL), McDonald's (OE), and the Ritz-Carlton (CI) serving as iconic examples of each approach. But the digital leaders shown in the figure typically excel in all three dimensions. For example, Amazon and Netflix have the widest product selection, the most efficient operations, and the most personalized customer experience in their respective markets.

Today's digital giants can do this because they replace costly human services with scalable digital ones. (It's another example of why we should use the term 'services' carefully, as the economics of human and online services are so fundamentally different.) This merger of the three value disciplines has further strengthened today's winner-take-all tendencies. Where once there was room for three market leaders, now there is often just one. It's a fundamental shift.

7.   Michael Treacy and Fred Wiersema, *The Discipline of Market Leaders,* Perseus Books, 1995

A digital platform IS the customer and/or user experience (CX/UX)

The digital CX/UX experience

1. Real-time, 24x7 operations

2. Automated, self-service support

3. Personalized recommendations

4. Ratings/reviews

5. Detailed account histories

6. Location awareness, tracking

7. Process and price transparency

8. Customization, co-creation

9. Community, ecosystem content

10. Global consistency

Even within traditional firms, the boundaries between sales, marketing, delivery, and customer support are often fuzzy; but on the internet, they typically vanish altogether, as everything happens through a single web site or app. As suggested by the figure, the digital platform is inseparable from the customer and/or user experience (CX/UX), as it defines what the customer sees and does.

For example, is a movie recommendation from Netflix a sales pitch, a marketing campaign, or a form of customer service? Who really cares? Since on the web pretty much everything works in a self-service mode, similar functional overlaps exist in most of the areas listed in the figure. How many of us have talked to any sales, marketing, or support person at any of today's digital giants, even once?

It's hard to exaggerate how different this is from the situation in most traditional firms, where sales, marketing, service, and logistics have grown up as separately staffed functions, with their own charters and positions to consider. Who hasn't run up against these silos when calling (for example) their bank, airline, phone, or cable company and been shuffled from one confused, even if well-meaning, department to another?

As the digital boundaries between functions fade away, the way that companies develop new capabilities must also change. It's not a coincidence that today's digital leaders are embracing more collaborative and multi-functional software development processes, as discussed further on the next page.

Digital platforms require team-based development approaches

Amazon's two-pizza approach:

"Software development should be a
collaborative, creative act"

- Team members are specialists, but collaborative
- Leaders are poly-skilled
- Teams self-manage and are collectively accountable
- Teams may eject members who can't fit in
- Teams use agile tools and APIs instead of traditional waterfall approach
- Advanced firms seek to hire whole teams

People often ask how Amazon keeps adding new services while maintaining such a consistent and intuitive customer experience. The company does many things well, but Amazon sets great store by its *two-pizza* development model. Its key product/service development teams should be able to feed themselves with a maximum of two pizzas (i.e. they should have no more than 12 people).

By setting up small, multi-functional teams, but also insisting on strict architectural discipline – mostly through web standards and APIs – Amazon has been able to sustain high rates of both innovation and integration, without any real burden on the customer.

But Amazon certainly isn't alone. The traditional waterfall approach (where business units hand over a fixed set of technology development specifications to Enterprise IT) is being replaced by the team-based model shown in the figure. For example, we know a digital media company where editorial, design, IT, marketing, analytics, and customer experience professionals build apps as a single, collectively accountable unit.

The leaders of such teams typically need to be *poly-skilled* so that they can both manage and earn the trust of team members. And while poly-skilled people can be hard to come by, the need for them will only increase. As technology permeates every organization, more collaborative, platform-based development approaches will be embraced by digital-first and pre-digital firms alike.

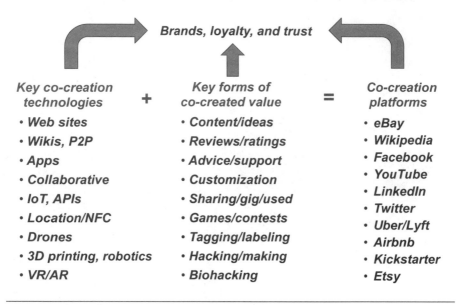

Co-creation platforms harness the crowd and the customer

Brands, loyalty, and trust

Key co-creation technologies		Key forms of co-created value		Co-creation platforms
	+		**=**	
• *Web sites*		• *Content/ideas*		• *eBay*
• *Wikis, P2P*		• *Reviews/ratings*		• *Wikipedia*
• *Apps*		• *Advice/support*		• *Facebook*
• *Collaborative*		• *Customization*		• *YouTube*
• *IoT, APIs*		• *Sharing/gig/used*		• *LinkedIn*
• *Location/NFC*		• *Games/contests*		• *Twitter*
• *Drones*		• *Tagging/labeling*		• *Uber/Lyft*
• *3D printing, robotics*		• *Hacking/making*		• *Airbnb*
• *VR/AR*		• *Biohacking*		• *Kickstarter*
				• *Etsy*

Many of the great digital platform successes – Apple, Amazon, Google, Microsoft, Netflix – are essentially broadcast in nature, in that the way one person uses these services isn't directly affected by the way that others do.

In contrast, co-creation platforms, while sharing many digital platform traits, differ in one fundamental way: the main value that these services provide comes mostly from other people using the service – examples include Facebook, Uber, eBay, Airbnb, and LinkedIn. This dynamic creates powerful *network effects* in that the more people who use the service, the more valuable it becomes. While we refer to this process of harnessing the knowledge, interests, and energies of the consumer as *co-creation*, other widely used names include social platforms, peer-to-peer, the crowd, two-sided markets, n-sided markets, and the sharing economy.

As shown in the figure, there is an overall co-creation formula. It starts with a powerful and growing list of enabling technologies, which can be used to create the various forms of value shown in the middle of the figure. Those co-creation vendors, organizations, or other entities that can become the go-to place for bringing together these technologies and forms of value, tend to dominate their category, with strong brands and customer loyalty. Once again, it's mostly a winner-take-all pattern.

Today, we see significant co-creation potential in virtually every industry, and thus when companies talk about becoming a *platform organization*, it's important to keep this *customer-as-means-of-production* dimension in mind.

Expect important new co-creation platforms to steadily emerge

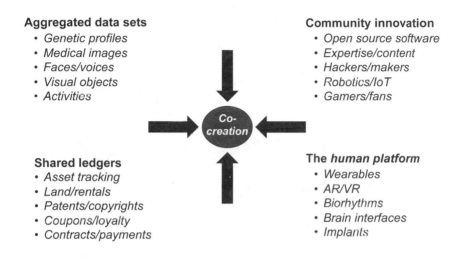

Aggregated data sets
- *Genetic profiles*
- *Medical images*
- *Faces/voices*
- *Visual objects*
- *Activities*

Community innovation
- *Open source software*
- *Expertise/content*
- *Hackers/makers*
- *Robotics/IoT*
- *Gamers/fans*

Shared ledgers
- *Asset tracking*
- *Land/rentals*
- *Patents/copyrights*
- *Coupons/loyalty*
- *Contracts/payments*

The *human platform*
- *Wearables*
- *AR/VR*
- *Biorhythms*
- *Brain interfaces*
- *Implants*

As described in Chapter 1, technology innovation tends to come in waves. During the web era (1993-2005), the emphasis was on email, search, browsing, and eCommerce, while the cloud era (2006-2016) saw the rise of mobility, social media, and the sharing economy. Since each previous era created important new companies and business models, it's only logical that the Matrix era will do the same.

Looking ahead, we believe that major new firms will emerge from the need to harness data and machine learning more effectively, and to better reward the social structures that underpin today's technology industry, as depicted above and explained below:

- Most MI capabilities/APIs will be based on a particular data set, and the companies that control such sets will have powerful market positions.
- Shared ledger systems will serve as the databases, payment systems, and legal platforms of the future, once again creating powerful new market players.
- We expect efforts to monetize at least some open source and other community projects, perhaps through digital tokens or initial coin offering (ICO) models.
- As will be discussed in Chapter 9, during the 2020s, innovation will increasingly shift to the human platform, augmenting both our brains and bodies.

Although these futures are still uncertain, co-creation thinking can help us see how new platforms might emerge over the course of the 2020s, as expanded upon in this chapter's final three pages.

Industry structures tend to run in cycles – the automobile example

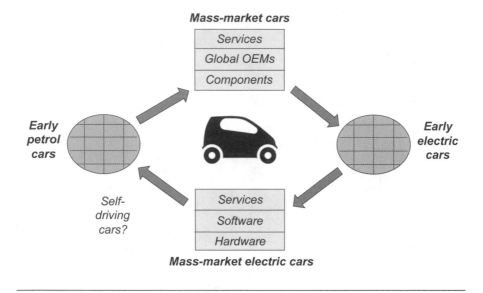

As we will discuss in Chapter 10, markets are always evolving, and no business model is ever permanent. Indeed, many industry structures are cyclical. Initially, a certain amount of vertical integration is often needed to get a functional new product to market (for example, remember the first iPhone or iPod), but over time, markets tend to specialize, as the range of customer needs increases and each component becomes a sizable opportunity of its own. But eventually, the underlying technologies shift, and the cycle begins anew.

The automobile industry embodies this pattern. As shown in the figure, in its early years, the Ford Motor Company was highly integrated, with its own steel, rubber, and shipping capabilities. But over time, the auto industry came to rely on specialized global supply chains, with Ford and other car makers playing the role of final system integrator.

However, with electric cars, vertical integration has returned, as shown by Tesla's huge commitment to making batteries and other components. Looking ahead, we are confident that once electric cars go mainstream, specialized component markets will once again emerge. Similarly, today's prototype self-driving vehicles require closely integrated capabilities, but these could easily separate into specialized hardware, software, and services if and when autonomous vehicles become a mainstream market.

Thus different markets tend to be in different stages of evolution, with newer models/structures/platforms emerging as older ones mature. Looking ahead, we expect many new technology platforms to emerge, as described on the next page.

Which models will underpin the technology platforms of the 2020s?

Business-centric		*Human-centric*

Business-centric
- *Internet of things*
- *3D printing*
- *Robotics*
- *Shared ledgers*
- *Digital cash/tokens*
- *Drones*
- *Precision farming*
- *Printed electronics*
- *Autonomous vehicles*
- *Quantum computers*

Human-centric
- *Wearables*
- *AR/VR*
- *Personalized learning*
- *Personalized medicine*
- *Genetic profiles*
- *Brain interfaces*
- *Emotion analytics*
- *Synthetic food*
- *Implants/prosthetics*
- *Biorhythms*

We will discuss in Chapter 11 how the media is often pessimistic about the digital future. But since we expect a great many new industries to emerge, and with them great opportunities and careers, we mostly disagree. While each of the areas above – and many others – are complex topics, we think the platform models described in this chapter can help us think about how each of these areas might evolve. For example, for each technology we might want to ask ourselves:

- To reach critical mass, does this technology need important innovation on multiple fronts – say in devices, software, and initial applications? If so, a vertically integrated iPod/iTunes/Tesla-like model might be needed.
- Is there an existing market or ecosystem that a new technology can naturally fit into? If so, a specialized, horizontal focus should generally work best.
- Is this an area that doesn't really require the adoption of new devices or any form of direct human support? If so, this market will likely follow the digital-first model.
- Is this market dependent upon collecting data in some new way or harnessing the knowledge and energy of a particular community? If so, then some sort of co-creation dynamic will likely be needed.

As we will discuss in Chapter 10, while the future is often unknowable, there are things we can do to recognize and even anticipate the likely nature of change.

An expanding range of business paradigms – 1970-2030

	Integrated solutions	Horizontal specialization	Digital first	Co-creation N-sided
Industry structure	Integrated solutions	Horizontal specialization	Digital first	Co-creation N-sided
Business focus	In-house capabilities	Ecosystem leverage	Category leadership	Collective intelligence
Competitive advantage	Products and distribution	Targeted innovation	Scale/brand CX/UX	Network effects
Industry value chain	Proprietary, siloed	Global supply chain	End-to-end, digital	Crowd/P2P, sharing
Organizational culture	Inside-out	Extended enterprise	Customer-centric	Outside-in, social trust

1970 ➤ 2030

As we have discussed, the business, organizational, and technology models used in the digital world today can be viewed as platforms, as new capabilities are continually built on top of one another. The figure above shows the four main models we have identified and describes how each platform type has emerged over time.

It's important to keep in mind that the older eras don't go away, and having businesses at different stages of maturity is entirely normal. However, there is a distinct and ongoing shift in society's economic center of gravity as the digital and co-creation models enable the most potent new players, and as traditional firms seek to apply these models within their sectors. In general, the market is evolving from left to right.

Looking ahead, we expect further platform innovation, as companies build focused data sets to enable advanced machine learning; as blockchain-type technologies enable data to be aggregated, shared, and leveraged in new ways; as open communities experiment with new forms of monetization; and perhaps most powerfully, as the ability of technology to enhance the human platform becomes increasingly compelling. Technology progress always builds upon itself.

But as impressive as all of these developments will be, they too will be platforms upon which future value will be built. Since we all stand on the shoulders of those before us, don't expect the use of the word 'platform' to go away anytime soon.

Chapter 5

Building your firm from the outside in

In this chapter

- The Matrix requires a shift from inside-out to outside-in thinking
- Outside-in strategies are needed across the full Matrix *stack*
  1. Key uses of *public cloud* computing
  2. Key types of *Software-as-a-Service* applications
  3. Key forms of *eCommerce* services
  4. Key forms of *digital messaging* services
  5. Key typoo of *open Innovation*
  6. Key types of *internet of things* devices and applications
  7. Key *internet business models*
  8. Key forms of *customer co-creation*
  9. Key forms of Matrix-based *security and privacy* capability
- Key ways organizations can *contribute* to the Matrix
- Executive oummaiy of outside-in Matrix usage
- What are the main barriers to Matrix usage in your organization?

In this chapter, we will expand our platform thinking by looking more deeply at the many components that make up the Matrix. We have identified over 100 specific Matrix service areas and organized them into nine broad technology categories (shown in items 1 – 9 above). While each is a platform for future value creation, taken together, they define what we mean by becoming an outside-in organization, and provide a framework with which companies can assess their Matrix usage and contribution today and going forward. As we chose to put this chapter in a workbook-style format of checklists for readers to complete for themselves, on most of the pages we have left room for your own notes and additions.

The Matrix requires a shift from inside-out to outside-in thinking

Inside-out	*Outside-in*
• Internal capabilities	• Ecosystem resources
• Intellectual property	• Open source collaboration
• Customer consumption	• Customer co-creation
• Marketing programs	• Community/social content
• Packaged software	• SaaS applications
• Company data centers	• Public cloud
• Management/control	• Leadership/influence

As we wrote about in Chapter 1, the Matrix represents a shift in the IT industry's center of gravity. This is especially true for large organizations that grew up meeting most of their own business and computing needs, but now find themselves adjusting to ever-more capable ecosystems full of specialized players that can perform just about anything that a company might do for itself.

While there are many dimensions to this shift, the seven transitions above encompass the essence of what is occurring. The first four items are market-focused. Companies increasingly need to look to the external environment first in terms of gaining access to resources, leveraging intellectual property, or harnessing the time, knowledge, and enthusiasms of their customers. The next two items are more about IT infrastructure, while the last one suggests changes in management and leadership style.

But let's be clear: while small and new businesses are overwhelmingly moving to the cloud/Matrix, in large, established organizations the situation is more mixed. New applications, web sites, analytics, development and testing are steadily moving to the cloud, but most mission-critical production work is still staying *on-premises*, resulting in today's complex hybrid environments.

However, the bottom line is that virtually all consumer usage, most small business usage, and a major part of the enterprise workload are all migrating to the Matrix. While there will always be anecdotes about work coming back in-house, the overall market direction is clear.

Outside-in strategies are needed across the full Matrix *stack*

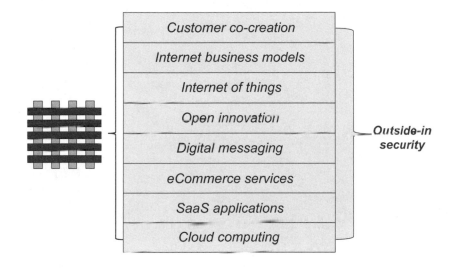

The figure above depicts what we mean when we say the Matrix increasingly mirrors the full range of business activity. The layers shown can basically be viewed as powerful and ready-to-go building blocks for 21st century organizations.

But the key challenge for most companies is to figure out how these external capabilities relate to what they are doing internally today. From a value and cost perspective, companies are asking themselves the following questions:

1. How can we harness the knowledge and energies of our customers?
2. Will digital technologies change our business model or value proposition?
3. Can we use IoT devices to create a smart and end-to-end value chain?
4. How do we tap into and leverage open source and crowd-based expertise?
5. What are the main ways we want to communicate, internally and externally?
6. Do we focus mostly on our own eCommerce site, or rely more on Amazon?
7. Does it make sense to convert large internal applications to a SaaS approach?
8. How much of our computing, back-up, and recovery can go to the cloud?
9. How do we manage the security challenges arising from all of the above?

The rest of this chapter is designed to help companies in each of these areas. (The security implications of this outside-in approach will be further addressed in Chapter 6.)

1) Key uses of *public cloud* computing

	Importance to your firm 1 = Low, 5 = High	Adoption strategy LE, FF, MM, LA, NA*	Skills 1 = Weak 5 = Strong	Future importance 1-5, DK*
IaaS	☐☐☐☐☐	☐☐☐☐☐	☐☐☐☐☐	☐☐☐☐☐
PaaS	☐☐☐☐☐	☐☐☐☐☐	☐☐☐☐☐	☐☐☐☐☐
Compute-intensive	☐☐☐☐☐	☐☐☐☐☐	☐☐☐☐☐	☐☐☐☐☐
GPU computing	☐☐☐☐☐	☐☐☐☐☐	☐☐☐☐☐	☐☐☐☐☐
Online storage	☐☐☐☐☐	☐☐☐☐☐	☐☐☐☐☐	☐☐☐☐☐
Back-up/redundancy	☐☐☐☐☐	☐☐☐☐☐	☐☐☐☐☐	☐☐☐☐☐
Data lakes/warehouses	☐☐☐☐☐	☐☐☐☐☐	☐☐☐☐☐	☐☐☐☐☐
Analytics/queries	☐☐☐☐☐	☐☐☐☐☐	☐☐☐☐☐	☐☐☐☐☐
Web hosting/streaming	☐☐☐☐☐	☐☐☐☐☐	☐☐☐☐☐	☐☐☐☐☐
Development/testing	☐☐☐☐☐	☐☐☐☐☐	☐☐☐☐☐	☐☐☐☐☐
Location/maps/SatNav	☐☐☐☐☐	☐☐☐☐☐	☐☐☐☐☐	☐☐☐☐☐
Production applications	☐☐☐☐☐	☐☐☐☐☐	☐☐☐☐☐	☐☐☐☐☐
Legacy app migration	☐☐☐☐☐	☐☐☐☐☐	☐☐☐☐☐	☐☐☐☐☐
Employee-owned devices	☐☐☐☐☐	☐☐☐☐☐	☐☐☐☐☐	☐☐☐☐☐
Other _____	☐☐☐☐☐	☐☐☐☐☐	☐☐☐☐☐	☐☐☐☐☐
Overall public cloud usage	_____	_____	_____	_____

* LE - Leading Edge   FF - Fast Follower   MM - Mass Market   LA - Late Adopter   NA - Not Applicable   DK - Don't Know

The next ten pages all use the format above. Each of the technology areas of the Matrix is broken down into its major components, and you are asked to rate your organization's usage of each component in terms of its importance today and in the future, as well as your current adoption strategy (leading edge, fast follower, mass market, or late adopter) and your current skill/experience level.

As company situations and the level of component maturity will often vary widely, there are no right or wrong answers, and not every area will be relevant to every firm. Our goal is simply to provide an objective snapshot of your organization's current Matrix situation, strategy, and skills. Since each component should be largely self-explanatory (or easily Googled), we have left a significant amount of space for you to jot down how these issues relate to your firm's situation.

_____

_____

_____

_____

_____

_____

2) Key types of *Software-as-a-Service* applications

	Importance to your firm 1 = Low, 5 = High	Adoption strategy LE, FF, MM, LA, NA*	Skills 1 = Weak 5 = Strong	Future importance 1-5, DK*
CRM (e.g. Salesforce)	☐☐☐☐☐	☐☐☐☐☐	☐☐☐☐☐	☐☐☐☐☐
Office 365 and similar	☐☐☐☐☐	☐☐☐☐☐	☐☐☐☐☐	☐☐☐☐☐
Collaboration (e.g. Slack)	☐☐☐☐☐	☐☐☐☐☐	☐☐☐☐☐	☐☐☐☐☐
Finance/ERP	☐☐☐☐☐	☐☐☐☐☐	☐☐☐☐☐	☐☐☐☐☐
Travel/expenses	☐☐☐☐☐	☐☐☐☐☐	☐☐☐☐☐	☐☐☐☐☐
HR/performance	☐☐☐☐☐	☐☐☐☐☐	☐☐☐☐☐	☐☐☐☐☐
Payroll/benefits	☐☐☐☐☐	☐☐☐☐☐	☐☐☐☐☐	☐☐☐☐☐
Recruitment	☐☐☐☐☐	☐☐☐☐☐	☐☐☐☐☐	☐☐☐☐☐
Surveys/focus groups	☐☐☐☐☐	☐☐☐☐☐	☐☐☐☐☐	☐☐☐☐☐
Learning/training	☐☐☐☐☐	☐☐☐☐☐	☐☐☐☐☐	☐☐☐☐☐
Compliance/CSR	☐☐☐☐☐	☐☐☐☐☐	☐☐☐☐☐	☐☐☐☐☐
Other _____	☐☐☐☐☐	☐☐☐☐☐	☐☐☐☐☐	☐☐☐☐☐
Overall SaaS usage	_____	_____	_____	_____

LE - Leading Edge   FF - Fast Follower   MM - Mass Market   LA - Late Adopter   NA - Not Applicable   DK - Don't Know

Software-as-a-Service has proved to have substantial advantages over traditional packaged software approaches in terms of ease of deployment, start-up costs, user interface/training, service upgrades, scalability, maintenance, and other areas, especially in the key application areas listed above. There tends to be a clear market leader in each category, and while these services can get expensive, their overall superiority seems very likely to prevail.

3) Key forms of *eCommerce* services

	Importance to your firm 1 = Low, 5 = High	Adoption strategy LE, FF, MM, LA, NA*	Skills 1 = Weak 5 = Strong	Future importance 1-5, DK*
Amazon	☐☐☐☐☐	☐☐☐☐☐	☐☐☐☐☐	☐☐☐☐☐
Mobile apps/app stores	☐☐☐☐☐	☐☐☐☐☐	☐☐☐☐☐	☐☐☐☐☐
Digital advertising	☐☐☐☐☐	☐☐☐☐☐	☐☐☐☐☐	☐☐☐☐☐
SEO services	☐☐☐☐☐	☐☐☐☐☐	☐☐☐☐☐	☐☐☐☐☐
Third-party resellers	☐☐☐☐☐	☐☐☐☐☐	☐☐☐☐☐	☐☐☐☐☐
Third-party delivery	☐☐☐☐☐	☐☐☐☐☐	☐☐☐☐☐	☐☐☐☐☐
Used market buying	☐☐☐☐☐	☐☐☐☐☐	☐☐☐☐☐	☐☐☐☐☐
Web hosting services	☐☐☐☐☐	☐☐☐☐☐	☐☐☐☐☐	☐☐☐☐☐
Internet payments	☐☐☐☐☐	☐☐☐☐☐	☐☐☐☐☐	☐☐☐☐☐
Mobile payments	☐☐☐☐☐	☐☐☐☐☐	☐☐☐☐☐	☐☐☐☐☐
Bitcoin	☐☐☐☐☐	☐☐☐☐☐	☐☐☐☐☐	☐☐☐☐☐
Blockchain	☐☐☐☐☐	☐☐☐☐☐	☐☐☐☐☐	☐☐☐☐☐
Other _____	☐☐☐☐☐	☐☐☐☐☐	☐☐☐☐☐	☐☐☐☐☐

Overall eCommerce usage _____ _____ _____ _____

* LE - Leading Edge FF - Fast Follower MM - Mass Market LA - Late Adopter NA - Not Applicable DK - Don't Know

The Matrix now provides a vast array of sales, marketing, delivery, and payment services. Indeed, Amazon by itself is by far the most important eCommerce utility in the western world today (in China, Alibaba dominates), which is why it is in a category of its own. Overall, companies increasingly need to be where the people are, and this means leveraging the major Matrix players, services, and platforms.

4) Key forms of *digital messaging* services

	Importance to your firm 1 = Low, 5 = High	Adoption strategy LE, FF, MM, LA, NA*	Skills 1 = Weak 5 = Strong	Future importance 1-5, DK*
Textual – email/IM/text	☐☐☐☐☐	☐☐☐☐☐	☐☐☐☐☐	☐☐☐☐☐
Audio – VOIP/Skype	☐☐☐☐☐	☐☐☐☐☐	☐☐☐☐☐	☐☐☐☐☐
Videoconferences, YouTube	☐☐☐☐☐	☐☐☐☐☐	☐☐☐☐☐	☐☐☐☐☐
Voice/speech	☐☐☐☐☐	☐☐☐☐☐	☐☐☐☐☐	☐☐☐☐☐
Online meetings	☐☐☐☐☐	☐☐☐☐☐	☐☐☐☐☐	☐☐☐☐☐
Facebook	☐☐☐☐☐	☐☐☐☐☐	☐☐☐☐☐	☐☐☐☐☐
Twitter	☐☐☐☐☐	☐☐☐☐☐	☐☐☐☐☐	☐☐☐☐☐
Other social	☐☐☐☐☐	☐☐☐☐☐	☐☐☐☐☐	☐☐☐☐☐
Feeds/RSS	☐☐☐☐☐	☐☐☐☐☐	☐☐☐☐☐	☐☐☐☐☐
Agents/bots	☐☐☐☐☐	☐☐☐☐☐	☐☐☐☐☐	☐☐☐☐☐
Bluetooth/iBeacon	☐☐☐☐☐	☐☐☐☐☐	☐☐☐☐☐	☐☐☐☐☐
RFID	☐☐☐☐☐	☐☐☐☐☐	☐☐☐☐☐	☐☐☐☐☐
Other _____	☐☐☐☐☐	☐☐☐☐☐	☐☐☐☐☐	☐☐☐☐☐
Overall digital messaging	_____	_____	_____	_____

* LE - Leading Edge   FF - Fast Follower   MM - Mass Market   LA - Late Adopter   NA - Not Applicable   DK - Don't Know

Today, there are so many ways to communicate that they often get in the way of one another, making it hard for any one form of messaging to gain critical mass. Perhaps the only thing for certain is that virtually all forms of digital messaging platforms have moved outside of the firm, as internal office phones and voicemail systems shrink in importance, and are sometimes removed altogether. Companies need to decide which communications platforms are most important to them, and steer and train their employees and customers accordingly. Many firms never really make up their minds.

5) Key types of *open innovation*

	Importance to your firm 1 = Low, 5 = High	Adoption strategy LE, FF, MM, LA, NA*	Skills 1 = Weak 5 = Strong	Future importance 1-5, DK*
Crowdsourcing	☐☐☐☐☐	☐☐☐☐☐	☐☐☐☐☐	☐☐☐☐☐
Free agent talent	☐☐☐☐☐	☐☐☐☐☐	☐☐☐☐☐	☐☐☐☐☐
Citizen scientists	☐☐☐☐☐	☐☐☐☐☐	☐☐☐☐☐	☐☐☐☐☐
Open source software	☐☐☐☐☐	☐☐☐☐☐	☐☐☐☐☐	☐☐☐☐☐
Open APIs	☐☐☐☐☐	☐☐☐☐☐	☐☐☐☐☐	☐☐☐☐☐
Open communities	☐☐☐☐☐	☐☐☐☐☐	☐☐☐☐☐	☐☐☐☐☐
Open RFPs	☐☐☐☐☐	☐☐☐☐☐	☐☐☐☐☐	☐☐☐☐☐
Open standards	☐☐☐☐☐	☐☐☐☐☐	☐☐☐☐☐	☐☐☐☐☐
Open data	☐☐☐☐☐	☐☐☐☐☐	☐☐☐☐☐	☐☐☐☐☐
Open designs/IP	☐☐☐☐☐	☐☐☐☐☐	☐☐☐☐☐	☐☐☐☐☐
Open 3DP	☐☐☐☐☐	☐☐☐☐☐	☐☐☐☐☐	☐☐☐☐☐
Other _____	☐☐☐☐☐	☐☐☐☐☐	☐☐☐☐☐	☐☐☐☐☐
Overall open innovation	_____	_____	_____	_____

* LE - Leading Edge   FF - Fast Follower   MM - Mass Market   LA - Late Adopter   NA - Not Applicable   DK - Don't Know

People have underestimated the power of open innovation and 'the crowd' since the earliest days of the internet. For example, many people once fiercely debated whether the internet could even survive without some form of centralized management control, just as they scoffed at the idea that Wikipedia would ever be a quality reference source. The same doubts are being voiced today about open source software, crowd sourcing, the maker movement, citizen science, Bitcoin, and other areas, even as overall outside-in innovation continues to grow. While it still sometimes seems counter-intuitive, decentralized innovation works in a wide range of areas.

6) Key types of *internet of things* devices and applications

	Importance to your firm 1 = Low, 5 = High	Adoption strategy LE, FF, MM, LA, NA*	Skills 1 = Weak 5 = Strong	Future importance 1-5, DK*
Smart products	☐☐☐☐☐	☐☐☐☐☐	☐☐☐☐☐	☐☐☐☐☐
Smart systems	☐☐☐☐☐	☐☐☐☐☐	☐☐☐☐☐	☐☐☐☐☐
Predictive maintenance	☐☐☐☐☐	☐☐☐☐☐	☐☐☐☐☐	☐☐☐☐☐
System optimization	☐☐☐☐☐	☐☐☐☐☐	☐☐☐☐☐	☐☐☐☐☐
Operational data	☐☐☐☐☐	☐☐☐☐☐	☐☐☐☐☐	☐☐☐☐☐
Video/still cameras	☐☐☐☐☐	☐☐☐☐☐	☐☐☐☐☐	☐☐☐☐☐
Sensors/RFID tags	☐☐☐☐☐	☐☐☐☐☐	☐☐☐☐☐	☐☐☐☐☐
VR/AR	☐☐☐☐☐	☐☐☐☐☐	☐☐☐☐☐	☐☐☐☐☐
Wearables	☐☐☐☐☐	☐☐☐☐☐	☐☐☐☐☐	☐☐☐☐☐
Drones	☐☐☐☐☐	☐☐☐☐☐	☐☐☐☐☐	☐☐☐☐☐
3D printers	☐☐☐☐☐	☐☐☐☐☐	☐☐☐☐☐	☐☐☐☐☐
Robots	☐☐☐☐☐	☐☐☐☐☐	☐☐☐☐☐	☐☐☐☐☐
Raspberry Pi, Arduino	☐☐☐☐☐	☐☐☐☐☐	☐☐☐☐☐	☐☐☐☐☐
Serverless	☐☐☐☐☐	☐☐☐☐☐	☐☐☐☐☐	☐☐☐☐☐
Other _____	☐☐☐☐☐	☐☐☐☐☐	☐☐☐☐☐	☐☐☐☐☐
Overall IoT usage				

* LE - Leading Edge   FF - Fast Follower   MM - Mass Market   LA - Late Adopter   NA - Not Applicable   DK - Don't Know

Many IoT devices are still in the relatively early stages of their innovation lifecycle. And as we saw in Chapter 3, the rate of adoption for most of these devices has been slower than for PCs, smartphones and other mass-market devices. Nevertheless, we remain bullish, as the devices above – and others – will be critical to our vision of an intelligent and connected society. In the short term, *predictive maintenance* is proving to be the driving IoT application, but over the long run, it's hard to bet against smart cities, smart grids, and the like.

7) Key *internet business models*

	Importance to your firm 1 = Low, 5 = High	Adoption strategy LE, FF, MM, LA, NA*	Skills 1 = Weak 5 = Strong	Future importance 1-5, DK*
Online sales	☐☐☐☐☐	☐☐☐☐☐	☐☐☐☐☐	☐☐☐☐☐
Service aggregation	☐☐☐☐☐	☐☐☐☐☐	☐☐☐☐☐	☐☐☐☐☐
Free services/trial offers	☐☐☐☐☐	☐☐☐☐☐	☐☐☐☐☐	☐☐☐☐☐
Mass customization	☐☐☐☐☐	☐☐☐☐☐	☐☐☐☐☐	☐☐☐☐☐
Algo operations	☐☐☐☐☐	☐☐☐☐☐	☐☐☐☐☐	☐☐☐☐☐
Gig/free-agent workers	☐☐☐☐☐	☐☐☐☐☐	☐☐☐☐☐	☐☐☐☐☐
Peer-to-peer/sharing	☐☐☐☐☐	☐☐☐☐☐	☐☐☐☐☐	☐☐☐☐☐
Crowd-funding, ICOs	☐☐☐☐☐	☐☐☐☐☐	☐☐☐☐☐	☐☐☐☐☐
Rewards/incentives	☐☐☐☐☐	☐☐☐☐☐	☐☐☐☐☐	☐☐☐☐☐
Auctions/reverse auctions	☐☐☐☐☐	☐☐☐☐☐	☐☐☐☐☐	☐☐☐☐☐
Games/contests	☐☐☐☐☐	☐☐☐☐☐	☐☐☐☐☐	☐☐☐☐☐
Prediction markets	☐☐☐☐☐	☐☐☐☐☐	☐☐☐☐☐	☐☐☐☐☐
Other _____	☐☐☐☐☐	☐☐☐☐☐	☐☐☐☐☐	☐☐☐☐☐

Overall business model use _____ _____ _____ _____

* LE - Leading Edge   FF - Fast Follower   MM - Mass Market   LA - Late Adopter   NA - Not Applicable   DK - Don't Know

Because they often directly challenge current practices, incentives, compensation schemes, and leadership, shifts in the business model are typically among the hardest for large organizations to adjust to, and thus can be highly disruptive. As discussed in Chapters 1 and 3, the Matrix offers powerful – but often unproven – new ways of selling, staffing, funding, and competing. This makes it an essential area for experimentation, and the open minds this requires. Among the areas listed above, ICOs are generating the most recent business-model buzz (and controversy). Think of them as Kickstarter with tokens.

8) Key forms of *customer co-creation*

	Importance to your firm 1 = Low, 5 = High	Adoption strategy LE, FF, MM, LA, NA*	Skills 1 = Weak 5 = Strong	Future importance 1-5, DK*
Content/ideas	☐☐☐☐☐	☐☐☐☐☐	☐☐☐☐☐	☐☐☐☐☐
Reviews/ratings	☐☐☐☐☐	☐☐☐☐☐	☐☐☐☐☐	☐☐☐☐☐
Advice/support	☐☐☐☐☐	☐☐☐☐☐	☐☐☐☐☐	☐☐☐☐☐
Instructional videos	☐☐☐☐☐	☐☐☐☐☐	☐☐☐☐☐	☐☐☐☐☐
New applications	☐☐☐☐☐	☐☐☐☐☐	☐☐☐☐☐	☐☐☐☐☐
Customization	☐☐☐☐☐	☐☐☐☐☐	☐☐☐☐☐	☐☐☐☐☐
Self-service	☐☐☐☐☐	☐☐☐☐☐	☐☐☐☐☐	☐☐☐☐☐
Sharing/gig	☐☐☐☐☐	☐☐☐☐☐	☐☐☐☐☐	☐☐☐☐☐
Tagging/labeling	☐☐☐☐☐	☐☐☐☐☐	☐☐☐☐☐	☐☐☐☐☐
Repairs	☐☐☐☐☐	☐☐☐☐☐	☐☐☐☐☐	☐☐☐☐☐
Problem solving	☐☐☐☐☐	☐☐☐☐☐	☐☐☐☐☐	☐☐☐☐☐
Other _____	☐☐☐☐☐	☐☐☐☐☐	☐☐☐☐☐	☐☐☐☐☐

Overall customer co-creation _____

* LE - Leading Edge   FF - Fast Follower   MM - Mass Market   LA - Late Adopter   NA - Not Applicable   DK - Don't Know

As discussed in Chapter 4, one of the reasons there is so much talk in the IT industry today about platforms is that every industry is trying to harness the knowledge, support, and enthusiasm of its customers. Indeed, many Matrix leaders – YouTube, Facebook, LinkedIn, Twitter, Uber, Airbnb – are almost entirely dependent on customer content and services. Looking ahead to a world of wearables, drones, implants, makers/hackers, and personalized medicine, the need for customer engagement and co-creation will only increase, as more and more value chains start to flow from the outside in.

9) Key forms of Matrix-based *security and privacy* capability

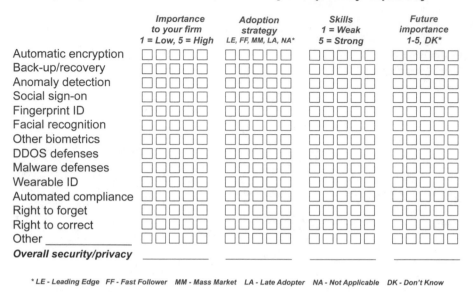

	Importance to your firm 1 = Low, 5 = High	Adoption strategy LE, FF, MM, LA, NA*	Skills 1 = Weak 5 = Strong	Future importance 1-5, DK*
Automatic encryption	☐☐☐☐☐	☐☐☐☐☐	☐☐☐☐☐	☐☐☐☐☐
Back-up/recovery	☐☐☐☐☐	☐☐☐☐☐	☐☐☐☐☐	☐☐☐☐☐
Anomaly detection	☐☐☐☐☐	☐☐☐☐☐	☐☐☐☐☐	☐☐☐☐☐
Social sign-on	☐☐☐☐☐	☐☐☐☐☐	☐☐☐☐☐	☐☐☐☐☐
Fingerprint ID	☐☐☐☐☐	☐☐☐☐☐	☐☐☐☐☐	☐☐☐☐☐
Facial recognition	☐☐☐☐☐	☐☐☐☐☐	☐☐☐☐☐	☐☐☐☐☐
Other biometrics	☐☐☐☐☐	☐☐☐☐☐	☐☐☐☐☐	☐☐☐☐☐
DDOS defenses	☐☐☐☐☐	☐☐☐☐☐	☐☐☐☐☐	☐☐☐☐☐
Malware defenses	☐☐☐☐☐	☐☐☐☐☐	☐☐☐☐☐	☐☐☐☐☐
Wearable ID	☐☐☐☐☐	☐☐☐☐☐	☐☐☐☐☐	☐☐☐☐☐
Automated compliance	☐☐☐☐☐	☐☐☐☐☐	☐☐☐☐☐	☐☐☐☐☐
Right to forget	☐☐☐☐☐	☐☐☐☐☐	☐☐☐☐☐	☐☐☐☐☐
Right to correct	☐☐☐☐☐	☐☐☐☐☐	☐☐☐☐☐	☐☐☐☐☐
Other _____	☐☐☐☐☐	☐☐☐☐☐	☐☐☐☐☐	☐☐☐☐☐
Overall security/privacy	_____	_____	_____	_____

* LE - Leading Edge FF - Fast Follower MM - Mass Market LA - Late Adopter NA - Not Applicable DK - Don't Know

While Chapter 6 will look at security more deeply and from a risk management perspective, it's clear from the list above that the Matrix enables both scary new threats and powerful new solutions. To succeed as a core societal infrastructure, the Matrix must eventually sustain the levels of societal confidence found in other critical national infrastructure areas – power, water, banking, telecommunications, defense, etc. While there is a long way to go, the decentralized and increasingly intelligent nature of the internet provides hope that an autonomous and self-healing digital Matrix will eventually emerge.

Key ways organizations can *contribute* to the Matrix

	Importance to your firm 1 = Low, 5 = High	Adoption strategy LE, FF, MM, LA, NA*	Skills 1 = Weak 5 = Strong	Future importance 1-5, DK*
Standards development	☐☐☐☐☐	☐☐☐☐☐	☐☐☐☐☐	☐☐☐☐☐
Standards support	☐☐☐☐☐	☐☐☐☐☐	☐☐☐☐☐	☐☐☐☐☐
Open source SW	☐☐☐☐☐	☐☐☐☐☐	☐☐☐☐☐	☐☐☐☐☐
Open IP	☐☐☐☐☐	☐☐☐☐☐	☐☐☐☐☐	☐☐☐☐☐
Open R&D	☐☐☐☐☐	☐☐☐☐☐	☐☐☐☐☐	☐☐☐☐☐
Open APIs	☐☐☐☐☐	☐☐☐☐☐	☐☐☐☐☐	☐☐☐☐☐
Open data	☐☐☐☐☐	☐☐☐☐☐	☐☐☐☐☐	☐☐☐☐☐
Industry consortia	☐☐☐☐☐	☐☐☐☐☐	☐☐☐☐☐	☐☐☐☐☐
Vertical clouds	☐☐☐☐☐	☐☐☐☐☐	☐☐☐☐☐	☐☐☐☐☐
Industry-specific services	☐☐☐☐☐	☐☐☐☐☐	☐☐☐☐☐	☐☐☐☐☐
Social sign-on use	☐☐☐☐☐	☐☐☐☐☐	☐☐☐☐☐	☐☐☐☐☐
Other _____	☐☐☐☐☐	☐☐☐☐☐	☐☐☐☐☐	☐☐☐☐☐

Overall Matrix contribution _____   _____   _____   _____

* LE - Leading Edge   FF - Fast Follower   MM - Mass Market   LA - Late Adopter   NA - Not Applicable   DK - Don't Know

While the discussion in this chapter thus far has been about how organizations can *use* the Matrix, would-be market leaders should also be thinking about how to better *build it out* in the areas shown above, and more. Think about the way, for example, that Visa is now cooperating with PayPal to improve digital and mobile payments. This *contribution* thinking is particularly relevant at an industry level, as each industry sector seeks to establish its own 21st century digital foundation. In this sense, we are all potential producers as well as consumers of advanced Matrix services.

_____

_____

_____

_____

_____

_____

Executive summary of outside-in Matrix usage

	Importance to your firm 1 = Low, 5 = High	Adoption strategy LE, FF, MM, LA, NA*	Skills 1 = Weak 5 = Strong	Future importance 1-5, DK*
1. Cloud computing	☐☐☐☐☐	☐☐☐☐☐	☐☐☐☐☐	☐☐☐☐☐
2. SaaS applications	☐☐☐☐☐	☐☐☐☐☐	☐☐☐☐☐	☐☐☐☐☐
3. eCommerce	☐☐☐☐☐	☐☐☐☐☐	☐☐☐☐☐	☐☐☐☐☐
4. Digital messaging	☐☐☐☐☐	☐☐☐☐☐	☐☐☐☐☐	☐☐☐☐☐
5. Open innovation	☐☐☐☐☐	☐☐☐☐☐	☐☐☐☐☐	☐☐☐☐☐
6. Internet of things	☐☐☐☐☐	☐☐☐☐☐	☐☐☐☐☐	☐☐☐☐☐
7. Internet business models	☐☐☐☐☐	☐☐☐☐☐	☐☐☐☐☐	☐☐☐☐☐
8. Customer co-creation	☐☐☐☐☐	☐☐☐☐☐	☐☐☐☐☐	☐☐☐☐☐
9. Security/privacy	☐☐☐☐☐	☐☐☐☐☐	☐☐☐☐☐	☐☐☐☐☐
10. Matrix contribution	☐☐☐☐☐	☐☐☐☐☐	☐☐☐☐☐	☐☐☐☐☐
Overall Matrix position	_____	_____	_____	_____

* LE - Leading Edge　FF - Fast Follower　MM - Mass Market　LA - Late Adopter　NA - Not Applicable　DK - Don't Know

Although our full list of over 100 Matrix components provides a much more complete picture, summary views can also be useful. As shown in the figure, aggregate Matrix ratings can provide a high-level management perspective that is currently not available within most firms today.

Since we have not yet gathered a lot of actual data, we don't have a clear sense of what constitutes an average score. Nevertheless, you can use this exercise to develop a sense of where your organization is in each area and why. Pay particular attention to how you stack up against current and emerging competitors. Any large gaps should be a source of discussion and possible concern. From our experience, some companies understand their competitors in these areas much better than others.

This summary can also help you describe your current technology situation, and how you might want to change it going forward. What will your Matrix usage look like in two, three, or five years? Does your overall technology adoption strategy need to change? Do your people agree or disagree on these issues?

Importantly, these are not just issues for the CIO or CTO; they affect the overall nature and culture of the firm. This is particularly the case in the upper levels of the stack, and their related skills and talent. As just about every organization (other than the GAFA) faces talent challenges, establishing a consensus in these areas is advised.

What are the main barriers to Matrix usage in your organization?

		Low barrier			High barrier	
		1	2	3	4	5
1.	Lack of speed/performance	☐	☐	☐	☐	☐
2.	Lack of control, ownership, trust	☐	☐	☐	☐	☐
3.	Data protection/location concerns	☐	☐	☐	☐	☐
4.	Finance/cost/ROI concerns	☐	☐	☐	☐	☐
5.	Regulatory requirements	☐	☐	☐	☐	☐
6.	Legacy system rigidity	☐	☐	☐	☐	☐
7.	Lack of internal skills/awareness	☐	☐	☐	☐	☐
8.	Overall risk/uncertainty	☐	☐	☐	☐	☐
9.	Company inortia/culture	☐	☐	☐	☐	☐
10.	Other _____	☐	☐	☐	☐	☐

Despite all their success so far, cloud and SaaS revenues are still only a fraction of the vast enterprise computing marketplace. While we are very bullish on the prospects for the firms supplying these services, we need to ask ourselves why change is often so hard. As noted earlier, within traditional firms, most of the work done on (for example) Amazon's AWS is still what could be called peripheral – such as new applications, development and testing, streaming media, analytics, and back-up. The vast core of legacy applications remains largely untouched.

But it was ever thus. IT applications tend to stay where they are, with new work being done in new ways. For example, personal computers didn't change the core work of mainframes; they did offload certain peripheral applications, but their real impact was enabling entirely new forms of individual computing. The same has been true for the smartphone's impact on the PC. There is a big difference between superseding and replacing.

This is what we are seeing today. Consumer, small business, and new enterprise work is migrating to the Matrix and creating a new industry center of gravity, even as much of the traditional IT legacy stays put. Thus the key question isn't how the barriers listed above affect the future of your legacy; it's whether they are preventing your firm from finding its future. The most important technology innovations of the 21st century will increasingly come to you from the *outside-in*.

Chapter 6

Seeing technology's risks

In this chapter

- Risk is business; business is risk
- We see three main types of computer technology risk
- *Cyber risks* are still on the rise
- Critical national infrastructures remain vulnerable
- The Matrix will improve cyber security from the outside-in
- Reducing *digital risk* requires a broad-based trust agenda
- Transparency can both increase and decrease digital risks
- Who is responsible for mitigating digital risks?
- *Information risks* are harder to see, and thus more insidious
  1. Information overload is just getting started
  2. Human judgement is subject to systematic errors and biases
  3. Observer and gaming effects often undermine stated goals
  4. Computerized systems nurture and mask business risks in subtle ways
- New forms of digital insurance and assurance will be required
- As the future will never be predictable, risk will always be with us
- A 12-step agenda for seeing risk

Moving to the Matrix is clearly not without its risks. In this chapter, we will break down computer technology risks into three main categories: deliberate 'cyber' attacks, the unintentional misuse of 'digital' capabilities, and the insidious uncertainties and incompleteness of 'information' itself. While these risks can never be eliminated, they can often be mitigated.

Risk is business; business is risk

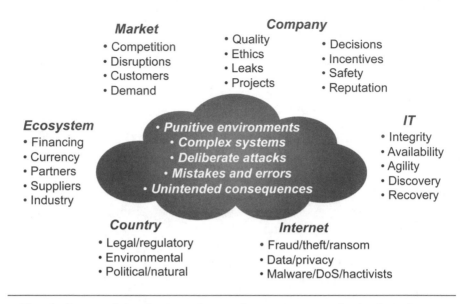

The challenge of developing a comprehensive way to think about business risk is depicted in the figure above, which shows the pervasiveness of potential business and information concerns. When we present this picture to clients, the most common response is "yeah, we face all of those challenges."

Many clients tell us that while identifying the major areas of risk is relatively easy, it's much more difficult to compare one risk to another, and even harder to bring them into any sort of holistic, prioritized picture that isn't overwhelming to the project participants. In other words, most companies struggle to think about risk systematically.

While the six categories around the perimeter are worrisome enough, the factors in the middle create additional challenges. We live in an increasingly punitive business environment (at least in terms of company fines and damaged reputation, if not personal/executive accountability) that often seems at odds with the vast uncertainties of the digital world. Even the best-intentioned organizations face many forms of system complexity and behavioral dynamics that virtually assure unintended consequences.

The net effect is that while formal risk management systems and processes are important, and MI will help, informed human judgment is still the core risk management competency. As businesses are based upon risk-taking, the idea of *riskless business* is essentially an oxymoron. This means that while risks can be managed and mitigated, they can never be eliminated. Business and risk are two sides of the same coin.

We see three main types of computer technology risk

Cyber risks:
Intentional attacks and damage

Each type requires a different strategy and mindset

Digital risks:
Unintentional
failures and mistakes

Information risks:
Insidious
second-order effects

The word *risk* has many different connotations. To most of us, the first associations are negative – loss, liability, failure, embarrassment, etc. From this perspective, the overall message is one of caution, or just saying 'No.' But others, especially entrepreneurs, have a view of risk that is much more positive: win, reward, adventure, chance, excitement, and so on. For such people, risk-taking is about saying 'Yes.'

Social science research has long demonstrated that most people feel worse about losing $100 than they feel good about winning the same amount. This explains why most of us are not well suited to be entrepreneurs: we are too risk-averse. But both risk avoiders and risk takers can benefit from using a common set of risk terminology, such as that provided below:

- **Cyber risks** come from some form of *deliberate* attack from an individual, organization, nation, or other entity.
- **Digital risks** include failures, mistakes, misuse, and other problems *unintentionally* caused by customers, suppliers, technologies, or employees.
- **Information risks** come with our reliance on complex information systems. They include often *hidden* forces such as information overload, human biases, system inter-dependencies, and second- and third-order observer and gaming effects.

This chapter will look at each of these three areas in turn.

Cyber risks are still on the rise

1. **Theft** – *Monetary, intellectual property, trade secrets, confidential information …*

2. **Sabotage** – *Intentional breaking, damaging, or misusing systems and information*

3. **Fraud** – *Identity theft, spoofing, phishing, fake news, fake web sites …*

4. **Denial of service** – *High-volume attacks that overwhelm a system's capacity*

5. **Malware** – *Unauthorized software that enables remote control or damage of systems*

6. **Ransomware** – *Extorting money, typically to regain control of systems and/or data*

7. **Leaks** – *Making information public to harm or embarrass a person or organization*

8. **IoT** – *Compromising or taking control of an internet-connected machine or device*

9. **Hackers** – *Finding hidden inner-workings, dependencies, and back doors*

10. **Hacktivism** – *Any of the above done by motivated people for a 'cause'*

Today, cyber-attacks get most of the IT risk attention, and understandably so. The list of high-profile damage is growing – Sony, Equifax, Yahoo, WannaCry victims, the Democratic National Committee, Ashley Madison, and many more. While inadequate awareness of vulnerabilities, poor system maintenance, and naive consumer/employee behavior have all played enabling roles, the bottom line is that few organizations can withstand sustained attacks from knowledgeable and well-funded entities. There are four main reasons why these cyber risks have grown sharply in recent years:

- **Proliferating tools.** Both the tools – such as Tor, Shodan, and I2P – and the instructions for cyber-attacks and the *dark web* are widely available.
- **The internet of things.** The IoT has provided a rich set of new targets, as many connected devices were not designed with strong security in mind. Cars, televisions, refrigerators, and even fish tanks have all been taken advantage of, and IoT usage and volumes have yet to reach the knee of the adoption curve.
- **Bitcoin.** Cryptocurrencies can provide criminals with convenient and anonymous payments, outside of traditional financial system control.
- **International anonymity.** Governments and other entities have learned that valuable business and political information can be inexpensively gained through cyber means, while also maintaining *plausible deniability*.

Most of these trends and threats are still moving in the wrong direction, leading to the societal risks and fears summarized on the next page.

Critical National Infrastructures (CNIs) remain vulnerable

1. Banking, trading, and payment systems

2. Electrical grid and power stations

3. Landline and mobile telecom networks

4. Space, satellite, and GPS systems

5. Terrestrial and air traffic control systems

6. Dams, canals, and water systems

7. Hospitals and healthcare systems

8. Voting and registration systems

9. Military and government systems

10. The internet itself

How can firms plan for –

or insure against – CNI

outages, corruption, or

loss of control?

Would your firm fare

better or worse than its

competitors

if CNIs were

compromised?

Just looking at the list of critical national infrastructures (CNIs) above is scary. In most nations today, no one can say for sure whether such systems could be, or already have been, compromised. Even the loss of one such system could be catastrophic, but imagine if most or all suddenly ceased working, or worked in unpredictable and/or inappropriate ways. Our dependency on technology has clearly created major societal risks.

These threats can be grouped into three main areas: system availability, information integrity, and outright warfare. With the electrical power, telecommunications, and transportation infrastructures, we need to be able to isolate such systems from the internet if necessary to assure availability. (Recent natural disasters have reminded us that battery-powered radios remain a vital form of reliable mass communication.)

While reliable power, telecommunications, and transportation are obviously critical, banks, hospitals, insurance companies, governments, and other key institutions are arguably at even greater risk from attacks that damage information integrity. Imagine the chaos if these institutions could no longer assure the accuracy of their information.

Lastly, there is outright cyber warfare. Should one nation be able to cripple or take control of the systems of a rival nation, they might not need to fire a single shot to assert their will. Unfortunately, given the many rivalries around the world, it's hard to imagine that such conflicts can be fully avoided. In the event of a critical infrastructure attack or collapse, how would your organization fare?

The Matrix will improve cyber security from the outside in

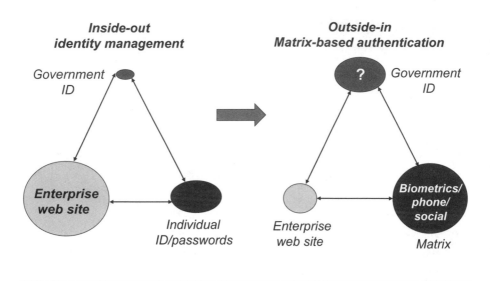

While it's easy to be pessimistic, the answer to the risks of technology dependency will likely be even more technology dependency. As IT usage shifts from inside-out to outside-in, the security challenge shifts from the demand to the supply side of the IT industry, and, while this is no panacea, it offers significant hope.

For example, with their vast resources and expertise, Amazon and Akamai are much better able than any individual firm to identify and counter a distributed denial of service (DDoS) attack, just as Microsoft, Symantec, and others in the field are better positioned to protect our Windows PCs. Overall, the major cloud vendors are now much better at IT security than most businesses and government agencies. They have to be.

An example of this supply-side approach is shown in the figure above. Today, the web relies heavily on user IDs and passwords, despite their obvious shortcomings. But user 'authentication' is now becoming a supply-side task. Biometrics, social sign-on, and phone-based approaches, perhaps backed by some sort of government digital ID process, will be vastly superior to authentication today. It's an area where the US generally trails, largely through lack of public and private cooperation. A key part of our Matrix metaphor is that the digital infrastructures of the future will be intelligent, aware, decentralized, and self-healing, and this makes us optimistic. But external attacks are not the only technology risks. Many problems stem from our own digital usage, as discussed next.

Reducing *digital risks* requires a broad-based trust agenda

1. **Product trust** – *Ratings, reviews, likes, support, instruction, advice, videos …*

2. **Transaction trust** – *Authentication, anomalies, detection, blockchains …*

3. **Reputational trust** – *Endorsements, followers, recognition, credentials …*

4. **Identity trust** – *Social sign-on, facial, iris, voice, fingerprints, gait, blockchain …*

5. **Software trust** – *Open source projects and code, methodologies, testing …*

6. **Scientific trust** – *Open review, open access, open methods, open data …*

7. **Business trust** – *Transparency, responsiveness, leadership, CSR …*

8. **Privacy trust** – *Right to correct/forget, custom privacy settings, permissions …*

9. **Value trust** – *Data usage, fair use, fair compensation, fair competition …*

10. **Technical trust** – *Encryption, auto-patching, firewalls, back-up, recovery …*

Risk and trust can be seen as two sides of the same coin. Each of the areas listed above is a source of risk, but one that can be mitigated through the various italicized items. The key message of the figure is that technology is enabling important new forms of digital trust across pretty much the full operational stack.

As will be discussed further on the following page, trust often boils down to increased *transparency* – the ability of customers to know what other customers think; to be able to understand exactly how their underlying software works; to have an immutable record of individual transactions; to understand the factual basis behind a claimed scientific finding; to be able to verify that people are who they say they are; and so on.

While most of the above items are either self-explanatory or have been discussed elsewhere in this book, *value trust* might need clarification. Do consumers think they're getting a fair deal in the way their information is used by suppliers for advertising and other purposes? Or does the pendulum need to swing back a bit so that customers can better control their own data, and perhaps receive a share of any monetization that occurs?

Taken together, the figure can help organizations see the nature of digital trust across their ecosystem. How does your organization fare? Which areas are most/ least relevant – now and in the future? Does your firm think systematically in such terms?

Transparency can both increase and decrease digital risks

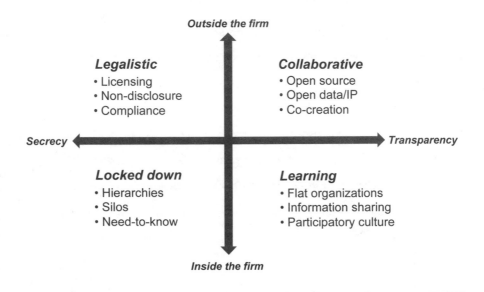

Protecting information is hard enough, but the challenge is compounded by the fact that businesses today are also expected to share information in ever-expanding ways. The figure above can help you find the right balance between secrecy and transparency, and internal and external information usage. We see four main approaches:

- **Legalistic.** Such firms limit external sharing, often relying on specific permissions such as non-disclosure agreements, licensing, and contracts.
- **Locked down.** These organizations share information internally on a need-to-know basis. They are likely to be hierarchical and/or siloed in nature.
- **Learning.** Such organizations seek to share information internally through flatter, more community-oriented, and participatory cultures. Although this can be difficult, many firms like to see themselves in this way.
- **Collaborative.** These firms work closely and co-create with a wide range of external organizations and/or individuals. They are leaders or participants in various 'open' initiatives.

Of course, most organizations are a mix of all four styles, but generally one predominates. No approach is necessarily better or more virtuous than the others. Consider that Apple is seen as locked down and legalistic, whereas Amazon and Netflix are more open. While there is an overall trend toward open innovation and open data, organizations will do whatever they consider best for them. The bottom line is that every organization has a de facto 'transparency strategy,' whether they know it or not.

Who is responsible for mitigating digital business risks?

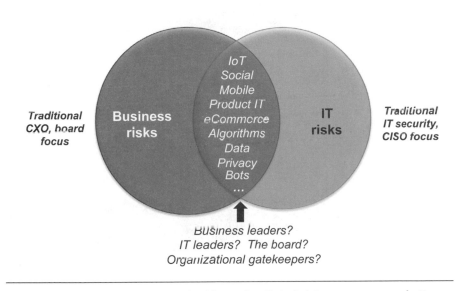

Traditional
CXO, board
focus

**Business
risks**

IoT
Social
Mobile
Product IT
eCommerce
Algorithms
Data
Privacy
Bots
...

**IT
risks**

Traditional
IT security,
CISO focus

Business leaders?
IT leaders? The board?
Organizational gatekeepers?

The previous two pages described how the digital risk management challenge has expanded to include many forms of marketplace trust, as well as the various approaches to information transparency. This raises the question of what the optimal risk management decision-making process should be. The recent scandals at Wells Fargo and Volkswagen clearly demonstrated that poor and unethical internal decision-making are even more dangerous than external cyber-attacks. The public will naturally feel at least some sympathy for firms that have been compromised through no clear fault of their own, but deliberately unethical behavior is another thing altogether.

While digital leadership will be explored more broadly in Chapter 7, here we just point out that, as shown in the figure, traditional lines of information security responsibility and business decision-making are blurring. The issues listed in the overlapped area are too close to the market to be the sole province of the CISO (Chief Information Security Officer), and too specific and technical for most executives and business leaders.

This argues for a team approach. We put particular emphasis on the need to also engage with *gatekeepers* – those parts of the firm that have an important control function, such as legal, audit, compliance, purchasing, quality control, and HR. Such groups and individuals should be brought in where appropriate to provide awareness of the full risk picture, and to build consensus around new digital initiatives.

Information risks are harder to see, and thus more insidious

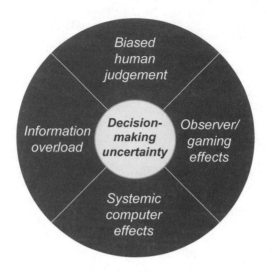

While many of the topics that we research are active areas of academic interest, few fields are as rich as risk management theory. In scanning the available literature, we came across a great many interesting books, journals, and thinkers, especially in the four areas shown above.

These *information risks* stem from both the rational and irrational sides of human behavior, as well as the dynamics of human and machine interaction. In this sense, information risks are neither *intentional* attacks, nor *unintentional* mistakes. They are embedded in the way things work, and thus are fundamentally more *insidious*. They are capable of creating risks in ways that are hard to counter, or even be fully aware of.

Consequently, each of the four areas above provides a different take on why there will always be a core of decision-making uncertainty, no matter how diligent or comprehensive the risk management process. Neither human knowledge nor computerized information is ever complete or perfect, and over time rationality often turns on itself. As we get deeper into a world of algorithms, measurement, rules, and autonomy, awareness of these second- and third-order forces will surely grow in importance. Over the next four pages, we will look at four different types of information risk, using technology's impact on the professions as a proxy for the broader question of how information processing and machine intelligence will ultimately affect many forms of human knowledge and decision-making. It's a fascinating area.

1) Information overload is just getting started

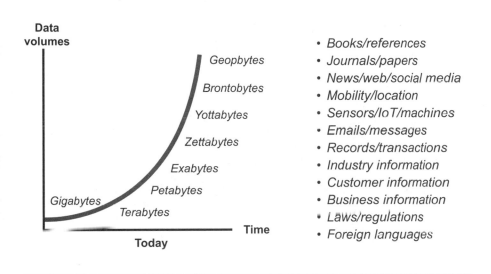

Data volumes

Geopbytes

Brontobytes

Yottabytes

Zettabytes

Exabytes

Petabytes

Gigabytes

Terabytes

Time

Today

- *Books/references*
- *Journals/papers*
- *News/web/social media*
- *Mobility/location*
- *Sensors/IoT/machines*
- *Emails/messages*
- *Records/transactions*
- *Industry information*
- *Customer information*
- *Business information*
- *Laws/regulations*
- *Foreign languages*

The trend that overwhelms the human is the trend that the machine thrives upon. As data volumes rise, humans can't keep up. With machines, it's the other way around: the more relevant data that is available, the better today's deep learning approaches perform. Today, few experts feel they can fully stay abreast of their fields, but machines aren't yet ready to fill the void.

Clearly, this challenge will get worse before it gets better. As shown in the figure, we are only at the knee of the data explosion curve, as the relevant information in just about every field continues to grow exponentially. Knowledge workers of all types say they are struggling with *information overload*, and this creates both risks and missed opportunities. Put bluntly: many generalists can't know all the relevant details, and many specialists can't see the overall picture.

Arguably, the only solution is for computers to be able to read *and comprehend* written materials, and then be able to provide needed knowledge on demand. But, as noted earlier, machine comprehension – while making progress and proving useful for recognizing words, clauses, tone, sentiments, outcomes, and similar slices of reality – has a long way to go before providing human-like *understanding*.

This still-growing inability to keep up helps explain today's noticeable erosion of traditional professional deference, a dynamic reinforced by our increasing awareness that even the experts have worrisome biases, as discussed on the next page.

2) Human judgement is subject to systematic errors and biases

- Over-reliance on societal stereotypes

- Over-reliance on personal experiences

- Over-reliance on recent events

- Desire to confirm existing opinions

- Lack of statistical/probability knowledge

- Over-reliance on gut feel

- Over-confidence, arrogance, priesthood

Will machines tend to correct or amplify these problems?

The so-called 'elites' are often under populist attacks these days, and we are reluctant to join this clamor too wholeheartedly. Highly educated professionals are clearly a pillar of advanced societies, and they have earned high levels of deference. When the stakes get high enough, even the most skeptical individuals almost always follow what their doctor, lawyer, or financial advisor recommends. (Politicians, economists, and social thinkers are another matter altogether.)

That said, professionals (and business executives) are human, and humans make mistakes. There is now a growing body of research on the systematic nature of human error. No one has done more to popularize this thinking than Michael Lewis, whose entertaining 2003 book[8] (and 2011 movie) *Moneyball* showed how baseball executives consistently mis-valued athletes by relying too much on 'gut feel.' The book triggered the explosion in data analytics across virtually all professional sports.

In his later book *The Undoing Project*[9], Lewis showed how both expert and non-expert decision-making suffers from the human tendencies listed in the figure. These seven areas manifest themselves in many ways, including undetected and unreported mistakes, inappropriate use of data and other evidence, and a troubling inconsistency in professional opinion across fields as diverse as medical diagnosis, taxation advice, scientific research, student grading, and criminal sentencing.

Properly used, data analytics can help identify and mitigate these biases. But as discussed on the following page, proper use can be tricky.

---

8.   Michael Lewis, *Moneyball: The Art of Winning an Unfair Game*, W W Norton & Co, 2003
9.   Michael Lewis, *The Undoing Project: A Friendship That Changed Our Minds*, W W Norton & Co, 2016

3) Observer and gaming effects often undermine stated goals

*Examples of systems that are
easily (inevitably?) gamed:*

- *Business bonus criteria*
- *Government targets*
- *Health and safety figures*
- *On-time departures*
- *Service level agreements*
- *Student test metrics*
- *Customer satisfaction data*
- *Financial industry reforms*
- *Environmental regulations*

Goodhart's Law:

"Any observed

statistical regularity

will tend to collapse

once pressure is placed on it

for control purposes."

The 17 words above from Professor Charles Goodhart[10] of the London School of Economics contain so many ideas that they need to be carefully unpacked. There are indeed many 'statistical regularities' (patterns) in business; some are 'observed' while others have yet to be identified. Companies naturally seek to use these patterns for various management 'control purposes.'

But 'once' this happens, the regularity itself will begin to 'collapse' because the motivations behind the individual actions that led to the regularity will have changed. In other words, individuals, whether consciously or unconsciously, inevitably seek to *game the system*, once new rules are in place.

These *observer effects* cut across just about every firm and industry. For example, we all know that employees managing budgets will move money around to better meet their bonus criteria; that companies almost make a sport of defining metrics such as *customer service response time* and *on-time flight departures* in ways that make them look good; and that the very act of writing a detailed contract can undermine the performance and assurance the contract is seeking. We heard, perhaps apocryphally, of one hospital that responded to the problem of too many people dying 'in surgery' by simply moving patients into 'the hallway' as soon as possible.

These effects are insidious in that they often emerge gradually, even invisibly. Companies clearly need rules and measurements. But they also need to be aware that while such regularities can reduce some business risks, they can easily spawn others.

---

10. Known as 'Goodhart's Law': C A E Goodhart, *Monetary Theory and Practice*, Macmillan, 1984

4) Computerized systems nurture and mask business risks in subtle ways

1. Computers are linear, but the world is non-linear
2. Computers treat information and data as discrete 'facts'
3. Classification creates a false sense of certainty and control
4. Automation often stifles lone voices, human judgement, and weak signals
5. Computers tend to squeeze out non-computerized information sources
6. Process automation can narrow how employees see their environment
7. Computers don't easily adapt to changing market conditions
8. Computers rarely account for second- and third-order effects
9. Computers are essentially a form of management bureaucracy
10. Computers start as an installation, and only over time become a 'system'

Perhaps the most insidious risks of computer automation are those that stem from the ten characteristics above, which we developed in conjunction with Professor Ian Angell at the London School of Economics.

We say this because these risks can occur even when an information system is operating exactly as planned. While each of the ten items above is worth pondering separately, the basic idea is that most computer systems rely on a simplified view of reality. Things need to be done in a certain way using agreed-upon information inputs, and this means that exceptions, nuances, related information, context, second-order effects, and skeptical voices tend to get squeezed out.

This over-simplification can easily lead to over-confidence, as an installed set of rules and capabilities is increasingly seen as an authoritative management system. This inability to deal with real-world complexity also helps explain why so many economic, financial, weather, political, environmental, and social models prove to be inaccurate. We don't say this to disparage such efforts – smart people are doing the best they can – but as Warren Buffet likes to say, we should "beware of geeks bearing formulas."

This warning will prove especially relevant going forward. Modern algorithmic operations also rely on intelligent, well-meaning simplification, and thus they tend to have the same underlying vulnerabilities. Algorithms can be very useful, and we will increasingly rely on them, but they will never capture the full complexity of the real world.

New forms of digital insurance and assurance will be required

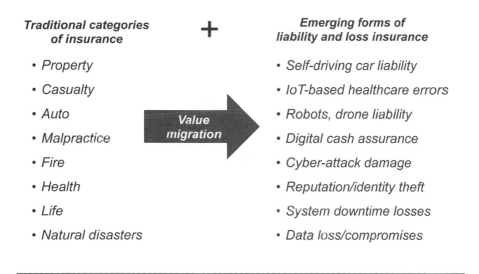

Traditional categories of insurance	+	Emerging forms of liability and loss insurance
• Property		• Self-driving car liability
• Casualty		• IoT-based healthcare errors
• Auto	Value migration	• Robots, drone liability
• Malpractice		• Digital cash assurance
• Fire		• Cyber-attack damage
• Health		• Reputation/identity theft
• Life		• System downtime losses
• Natural disasters		• Data loss/compromises

Every year, more than a million people die in car accidents. Once in a great while a passenger jet crashes or disappears. Industrial accidents are too numerous to be reported. Houses burn down; things get stolen; people get sick. Banks go bankrupt. Since we know these things will happen, but we don't know who they will happen to, vast public and private insurance markets have emerged.

As the virtual world grows and generates its own accidents, losses, and risks, new forms of digital insurance need to emerge in the areas shown above and more. Indeed, in areas such as self-driving cars and digital currencies, it's hard to see how these markets can ever reach critical mass without sound customer assurance in place. Whether these offerings will come from traditional insurance firms, or new players (perhaps, for example, the autonomous car firms themselves) remains to be seen.

Companies will also buy insurance to soften the blows from business disruption, data losses, reputational damage, digital liability, and other technology risks. And while we tend to think of insurance companies only when we need them, these firms play an important ongoing role in developing and requiring safer codes and practices, while helping to clarify who is legally responsible for what.

Eventually, digital risks should become as statistically predictable as other forms of loss, creating attractive insurance opportunities. But until then, lack of sufficient assurance could be a significant barrier to digital innovation and change.

As the future will never be predictable, risk will always be with us

1. How will the situation in North Korea be resolved?

2. What will the stock market average be tomorrow/in two years?

3. How much impact will climate change have by 2030?

4. Which political/economic views will rise and fall over the next few years?

5. Who is going to win the next big game/election?

6. What will be the next big trends in popular culture?

7. How will China's political system evolve?

8. What diseases and viruses will emerge as the biggest health risks?

9. What skills and jobs will be in most demand in the 2030s?

10. What will be the final balance between human and machine intelligence?

Many of our most important decisions are essentially bets on the future, as there are great rewards for those firms and individuals who can correctly anticipate market behavior, technology advances, geopolitical shifts, fashion trends, commodity prices, exchange rates, electoral results, environmental patterns, and other developments.

Digital enthusiasts often say that computer modeling will substantially improve our forecasting abilities, but the evidence isn't particularly persuasive. We think it is fair to say that computers are of little or no use in forecasting most of the big questions listed above, and there will always be *black swan*[11] developments that we haven't even thought of.

On the other hand, machines can be quite good at forecasting specific events – when a machine is likely to fail, the risks of a particular medical tumor, the results of a marketing campaign, insurance probabilities, and so on. But even though *predictive analytics* applications are rapidly expanding, they still leave us in a world where the decisions, interests, and passions of billions of individuals will determine our future in fundamentally unpredictable ways. As Yogi Berra artfully put it: "It's tough to make predictions, especially about the future."

This means that society will continue to need leaders and entrepreneurs to take risks, make bets, and try to shape the future to their ends. Indeed, the overall balance between people who are risk-takers and those who are risk-avoiders doesn't seem to change very much – perhaps it is even a cultural constant.

---

11. N N Taleb, *The Black Swan: The Impact of the Highly Improbable*, Random House, 2007

A 12-step agenda for seeing risk

1. Be aware of the full range of potential cyber-attacks, *Page 96*
2. Imagine what would happen if critical infrastructure(s) went down, *Page 97*
3. Think about how outside-in Matrix capabilities can improve security, *Page 98*
4. Identify areas where *digital trust* can be enhanced, *Page 99*
5. Develop a consensus on your *transparency* strategy, *Page 100*
6. Combine executives, IT, and key *gatekeepers* into a risk/reward team, *Page 101*
7. Determine where *information overload* is causing problems, *Page 103*
8. Use analytics as a check against professional and executive *bias*, *Page 104*
9. Account for *second-order* and *gaming* effects in key business metrics, *Page 105*
10. Understand how computer systems can over-simplify the real world, *Page 106*
11. Consider where insurance can help cope with technology risks, *Page 107*
12. Use *predictive analytics* mostly in specific, short-term areas, *Page 108*

The purpose of this chapter has been to help readers see the breadth of technology risk today – especially deliberate attacks, unintentional misuse, and the built-in downsides of simplifying the world into a binary system.

Readers might naturally say that, while seeing is a good first step, what about acting? We haven't said much about the specific things that firms should do, because risk management best practices are well covered by others, and in fast-moving markets, things change. Our goal has been more educational and conceptual in nature.

But clearly, companies are taking many actions to make their organizations more resilient and *less fragile*. These include: board-level education and discussions; multiple forms of cloud back-up; improving sensing and anomaly detection; assuring access to critical skills; hacking your own systems; decentralizing operations; increasing diversity; reducing groupthink; and developing a culture of safety and awareness.

In these areas, the goal isn't perfection, but being better than your competitors, as the most resilient firms tend to grow stronger when their sector is threatened. This ability to turn risks into competitive advantage is sometimes referred to as *anti-fragility*.

But as we said at the outset of this chapter, human judgement is still the core risk management competency. The future remains fundamentally unknowable, and thus organizations can never be sure what they will face. Hamlet basically had it right: *"The readiness is all."*[12]

---

12. William Shakespeare, *Hamlet*, Act V scene ii 237

Chapter 7

Digital leadership is a team sport

In this chapter

- The most famous IT leaders have always been on the supply side
- Digital leadership should be a team sport
- Board-level digital knowledge and awareness often lags
- CEOs ask: Who should lead digital?
- Digital leadership in the C-suite: Observed roles
- Digital leadership assessment: Senior executives
- *Double-deep* employees are well positioned to be digital leaders
- Digital leadership assessment: Employees
- Digital leaders bring the Matrix into their firm
- Digital leadership assessment: Matrix engagement
- Most IT professionals come from a back-office culture
- What type of CIO does your organization have?
- Digital leadership assessment: Enterprise IT
- A quick entrepreneurial leadership and culture check
- A leadership agenda for digital transformation

In this chapter, we argue that digital leadership should be a team sport. The key team members include senior executives, technology-savvy employees, the Enterprise IT organization, and selected business partners. High-level self-assessment exercises are provided to help define the state of each leadership source within your organization today.

The most famous IT leaders have always been on the supply side

Top 50 digital inventors and entrepreneurs, 1967-2017

Gene Amdahl, Ross Perot, Seymour Cray, Ted Codd,
Gordon Moore, Robert Noyce, Andy Grove, Vint Cerf,
Robert Khan, Ken Olsen, Gordon Bell, An Wang, Larry
Ellison, Hasso Plattner, Ray Kurzweil, Bob Metcalfe, Bill
Joy, Andy Bechtolsheim, Steve Wozniak, Steve Jobs,
Leonard Bosack, Don Estridge, Bill Gates, Mitch Kapor,
Al Shugart, Rod Canion, Michael Dell, Scott Cook, Ray
Ozzie, Tim Berners-Lee, Linus Torvalds, Tom Siebel,
Marc Andreessen, Steve Case, Mike Lazaridis, Jeff
Bezos, Shawn Fanning, Pierre Omidyar, Larry Page,
Sergey Brin, Marc Benioff, Elon Musk, Janus Friis,
Jimmy Wales, Reed Hastings, Mark Zuckerberg,
Reid Hoffman, Jack Dorsey, Travis Kalanick, Jack Ma

- **76% US born**
- **88% US educated**
- **78% college grads**
- **42% advanced degree**
- **78% firm founder**
- **56% worked mostly in California**
- **32 – average age when founder/inventor**
- **All men**
- **The next 50?**

Historically, the best known and most influential IT leaders have always come from the supply side of the industry – primarily inventors and/or entrepreneurs. Indeed, in the list we recently compiled of the 50 most important IT industry leaders of the last 50 years shown in the figure above, everyone either established important new technologies/capabilities or founded/co-founded a major technology firm.

The demographics of these leaders (shown at the right of the figure) are revealing, and tell us much about the technology industry's history. There has been a clear US dominance in terms of birthplace, but even more so in university education. Over time, there has been a shift from PhD inventors to college dropout entrepreneurs, and this has coincided with the group getting younger on average as the years go by.

Most noticeably, all 50 are men. This is obviously a sensitive point, but having circulated this list widely, we have seen no compelling evidence otherwise[13]. (We stress again that the list consists of technologists/founders, not appointed CEOs.) The much-debated reasons behind this pattern are a topic for another book, and we surely expect both the geographic and gender pattern to change substantially going forward. But the key question for our clients is how these supply-side patterns – entrepreneurship, invention, geography, youth, education, and gender – might relate to their own digital leadership situation.

---

13. Quite a few people mentioned Admiral Grace Hopper for her important work on machine-independent programming languages, but this work was done more than 50 years ago.

Digital leadership should be a team sport

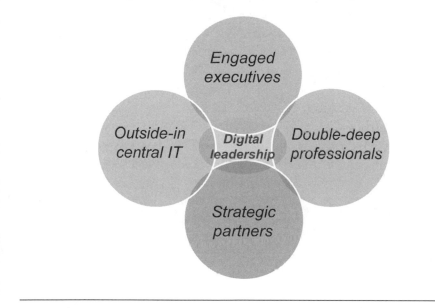

But whereas supply-side digital leadership has long been characterized by a relatively small number of individuals who have mostly become fabulously wealthy, inside the traditional firm, digital leadership is less glamorous, and much more of a process challenge. As depicted above, we believe that digital leadership should come from four main groups:

- **Executives** who believe that *IT matters*, and who accept that they need to take responsibility for their firm's major digital initiatives.
- **Tech-savvy employees** who embrace and even lead the adoption of new ways of working. We refer to employees who know both their individual job function and the relevant technologies as double-deep.
- **Strategic partners** who bring the latest Matrix services and other new ideas and capabilities into their customers' organizations.
- **An outside-in central IT organization** that helps drive the digital business agenda, while working closely with customers, partners, and suppliers.

While the mix of these requirements will vary across firms and industries, leadership from all four sources has proved to be important in just about every large organization we have worked with. Each area presents significant cultural and career challenges, but taken together, they largely determine the *digital IQ* of the modern enterprise. This chapter discusses these four groups and helps you assess the state of digital leadership in your organization.

Board-level digital knowledge and awareness often lags

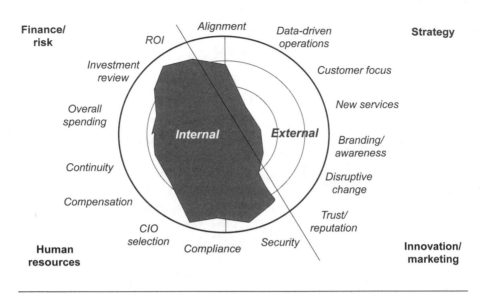

The figure above is taken from research we did a few years ago, examining how executives at the Board-of-Director level engaged with IT. The research showed that the majority of board attention was aimed at internal IT activities – spending, budgets, investment approvals, compensation, CIO succession, HR, auditing, compliance, and so on.

Relatively little time was spent looking at how IT was transforming the nature of competition and the marketplace, what it means to be data-driven, or how the company will be different in a digitally driven future. We recall one CIO telling us that he had always wanted to meet with the board – until he did, and saw how limited the IT conversations actually were.

We have no doubt that over the last few years this situation has improved significantly, as the importance of IT has become much more widely recognized. Many organizations today make an effort to have at least one technologist on their board, and it is now commonplace for companies to send senior and/or up-and-coming executives on various technology awareness programs. These days very few, if any, directors would say that "IT doesn't matter."

But while we know that the overall situation is improving, we also know that in many traditional firms, the board and the executive team are still at odds with the digital world, often resulting in a significant digital leadership shortage at the top table, as discussed over the next three pages.

CEOs ask: Who should lead digital?

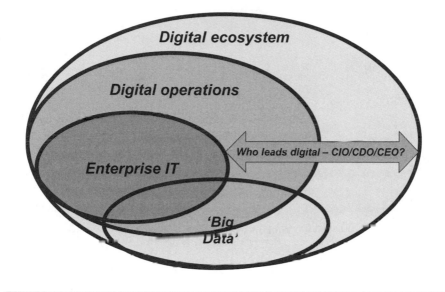

Digital leadership within the upper executive ranks is often a highly political topic. As shown in the figure, technology usage now extends far beyond the traditional scope of Enterprise IT, and cuts across most business operations and fiefdoms. Just about every company function is becoming digital, one way or another, and thus everyone in the C-suite needs to be a digital leader in some way.

Given this, the abdication of the entire digital agenda to the CIO or a Chief Digital Officer (CDO) is no longer advisable. In many firms, that approach is becoming the equivalent of retiring. But this reality creates obvious tensions. How many of the leaders of traditional firms are capable of making the transition to digital leadership? Is it even reasonable to expect highly successful executives in their 50s and 60s to be able to envision and lead complex digital initiatives? Do CEOs have confidence in their digital leadership team? How many current executives will need to be replaced?

Already, we see firms looking for new pools of leadership and talent, often in Silicon Valley itself. Companies are bringing in executives from firms such as Microsoft, Cisco, and Oracle because those individuals have grown up in the digital world and have a more intuitive sense of what digital transformation means. Organizations are also experimenting with various forms of digital education, reverse mentoring, and other tactics. But the fundamental question remains: *Who leads digital?*

Digital leadership in the C-suite: Observed roles

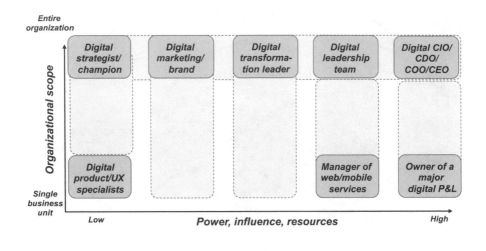

The complex nature of digital leadership in the C-suite is shown in the important figure above. The key roles are defined by the figure's two axes: how much authority does a person have, and how broad is the scope of this authority. We see five main approaches:

1. **Digital champions** are responsible for ideas, strategic vision, and related evangelism, but are often dependent on the CEO for actual authority.

2. **Digital marketing leaders** tend to have control over highly visible areas such as eCommerce, web/mobile, and social media, but not other forms of IT activity.

3. **Digital transformation leaders** are usually appointed to drive a particular high-profile technology or cultural initiative, typically for a two- or three-year period.

4. **Digital teams** are set up to make sure that key company executives work together, often under the authority of the CEO or COO.

5. **Chief Digital Officers** have been appointed in many organizations. Sometimes this person is the CIO, sometimes not.

Across the lower half of the figure are three other significant roles. Many firms have influential individuals who understand digital design and/or the customer experience, who run web or mobile systems, or who control a major digital P&L. Such people are often asked to play a broader digital leadership role at some point, and thus are an important source of talent, ideas, and thinking.

Digital leadership assessment: Senior executives

	Disagree 1 2 3 4 5				Agree

1. Senior leadership believes in the power of modern information technologies ☐ ☐ ☐ ☐ ☐

2. Senior executives accept that digital leadership is now part of their job ☐ ☐ ☐ ☐ ☐

3. Our senior leaders have the digital knowledge and experience they need ☐ ☐ ☐ ☐ ☐

4. Senior leaders are committed to being information- and data-driven ☐ ☐ ☐ ☐ ☐

5. Senior leaders provide positive examples of digital advocacy and adoption ☐ ☐ ☐ ☐ ☐

The questions above largely speak for themselves, and taken together should provide a good sense of whether an organization's senior leadership is playing a positive digital role. A few points about each question:

1. For many years, it was acceptable for top executives to have an 'I don't really care about technology' attitude. But this position is rapidly crumbling, and executives who take that stance find themselves increasingly isolated.
2. However, fully accepting that digital leadership is a core part of their job is still a bridge too far in many senior executive circles, sometimes rightly so, but often at their own career expense.
3. Senior executives often lack basic PC, mobile, and social media skills. Fear of embarrassment can prevent experimentation and learning that would otherwise occur. Reverse mentoring can help, but is not widespread.
4. Many executives pay lip-service to the idea of being data- and/or information-driven, because it sounds like something they ought to say. But most still prefer to trust their own gut feel.
5. The bottom line is that digital leadership means setting a powerful personal example. Without this, cultural change is difficult, and many companies fall short in this regard.

How well do your organization's senior leaders fare in these five areas?

***Double-deep* employees are well positioned to be digital leaders**

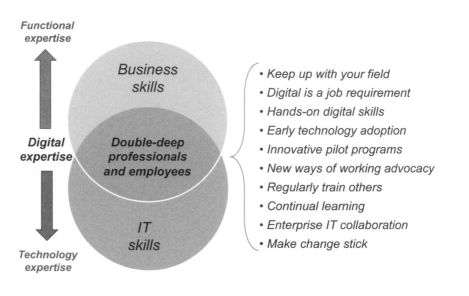

Way back in 2003, LEF began talking about *consumerization* – our view that the consumer marketplace was replacing large enterprises as the center of IT industry innovation. Consumerization means that most new technologies – indeed, the Matrix itself – now emerge from the *bottom up*, starting with consumers, then becoming more enterprise-focused over time.

This shift has important digital leadership implications. For many now widely used technologies (such as Microsoft Office, smartphones, social media, apps, collaboration tools, cloud storage, audio/video, etc.), the real experts in the company are as likely to be tech-savvy employees as any formal technology group or IT department members. These individual digital leaders need to be identified, leveraged, and rewarded.

More importantly, this bottom-up knowledge process is now reshaping work itself. As shown in the figure, the employees in most demand today are double-deep – capable of applying technology to a business need – marketing, accounting, engineering, customer service, etc. Double-deep employees are the ones who learn, adopt, and promote new ways of working, and help to make change stick. Employees who resist these changes are increasingly hard to promote, or even employ.

Ever since the personal computer era, firms have relied on what were then called *power users*: employees who embraced PCs and could help others do so. With the pervasiveness of technology today, such individuals are needed more than ever. Our key double-deep employee assessment questions are provided on the next page.

Digital leadership assessment: Employees

	Disagree				Agree
	1	2	3	4	5
1. Our employees accept the need to use technology in new ways to do their jobs better	☐	☐	☐	☐	☐
2. Our employees readily learn to use new IT tools, systems, and services	☐	☐	☐	☐	☐
3. Our employees feel empowered to experiment and use technology in different ways	☐	☐	☐	☐	☐
4. We have many employees who are digital leaders in their individual work areas	☐	☐	☐	☐	☐
5. Our employee digital leaders are adequately recognized and rewarded	☐	☐	☐	☐	☐

We recommend that organizations either conduct the above assessment (or our longer version) formally, or at least discuss the issues above informally. In many ways, employee attitudes to technology-driven change go a long way toward defining the digital culture of the firm, and from our experience many companies recognize that they have problems in this area, especially among older workers.

In contrast, firms that excel in these areas can use their culture as an important recruitment tool. A few comments about each question:

1. The 'I don't do IT' attitude is still widespread among employees in many firms. It must be resisted, and seen to be increasingly unacceptable.
2. In recent years, employee learning has shifted from formal training to *do-it-yourself*, and this puts an even greater premium on individual motivation.
3. Unless employees are permitted to do their work in new and better ways, their motivation to learn will eventually decline.
4. Most firms have employees who are widely seen as playing an important role in internal learning, evangelizing, and teaching. People know who they are.
5. It is essential that these people are recognized and rewarded for what can become a very time-consuming and difficult-to-measure role.

Some firms are clearly much farther along than others in these five areas.

Digital leaders bring the Matrix into their firm

1. **Awareness** – *Scouting Silicon Valley and elsewhere for trends, interesting start-ups, new technologies, and insights into the future*

2. **Openness** – *Participating in relevant open source projects, sharing information with key partners and even the marketplace at large*

3. **R&D access** – *Establishing and maintaining ties to leading universities, institutions, and/or government agencies in selected areas*

4. **Partnerships and alliances** – *Working effectively with the right set of firms for products, distribution, research, investments, and other areas*

5. **Digital culture** – *Energizing employees and executives through incubators, accelerators, hackathons, putting digital experts on the board, etc.*

Throughout this book we have stressed that the key dynamic in business today is the emergence of the increasingly intelligent, autonomous, and shared digital infrastructure that we call the Matrix. In Chapter 5, we identified the many different forms of outside-in innovation that companies should consider. But what does the Matrix mean for digital leadership?

Essentially, it means preparing to put the Matrix to work for your firm by doing all of the things shown in the figure. For example, just about every organization today has individuals who are more aware than others of what is happening in Silicon Valley and elsewhere, and some programmers who are drawn to the open source movement while others are not. We have been particularly impressed in recent years by the close relationships that many companies have with their local universities, both for experimental projects and as an ongoing talent pipeline.

But for many, the toughest Matrix leadership challenge is choosing who to work with. Whether you are in FinTech, MedTech, CarTech, or elsewhere, there is a dizzying array of interesting potential partners. Choosing a new partner is often very time-consuming, and this makes it difficult to evaluate all of the various alternatives.

The next page helps assess how well industry awareness, open source engagement, university collaboration, and effective business partnerships are helping your organization build a solid outside-in digital leadership culture.

Digital leadership assessment: Matrix engagement

	Disagree 1 2 3 4 5 Agree
1. We effectively track relevant new firms and technologies	☐ ☐ ☐ ☐ ☐
2. Our firm is good at external collaboration	☐ ☐ ☐ ☐ ☐
3. We are sufficiently open and transparent with our people, processes, and IP	☐ ☐ ☐ ☐ ☐
4. We are working with the right set of partners	☐ ☐ ☐ ☐ ☐
5. We are as good as or better than our major compotitors in these areas	☐ ☐ ☐ ☐ ☐

We have talked to many organizations about the increasingly outside-in nature of digital innovation. When we do this, most companies nod and see the logic of what we are saying. But turning abstract agreement into actual behavior change is difficult, and most companies acknowledge they can do much better in the areas listed above and expanded upon below:

1. While countless global companies have set up shop in Silicon Valley and elsewhere to be closer to new digital players, efforts to inject start-up DNA into the firm often prove disappointing.
2. Many companies realize that they don't collaborate well, and that their internal rules, practices, and supporting technologies can be unclear and/or overly rigid.
3. Firms still tend to keep their IP as proprietary as possible. Open source thinking remains mostly in the minds of digital engineers and software developers.
4. While nobody believes they can do everything by themselves, until the supplier space is less chaotic, many firms find it hard to act aggressively.
5. Companies generally have a sense of how they compare to competitors, but most seem to think that others are better than they are. They can't all be right.

Overall, establishing an outside-in innovation mindset remains a difficult organizational challenge. But as the Matrix becomes the business center of gravity in most industries, the need for this thinking will only increase.

Most IT professionals come from a back-office culture

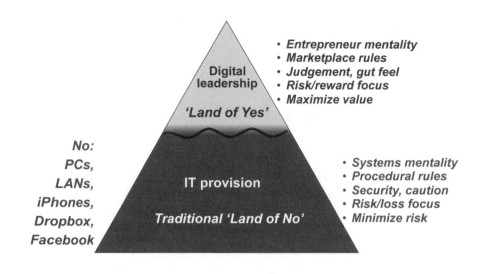

As we noted at the start of this chapter, the best-known IT leaders have always come from the supply-side of the industry, and this is still where the most ambitious and most entrepreneurial technologists tend to gravitate. This supply-side / customer-side career split typically begins quite early. While available local jobs certainly play a part, when young computer scientists graduate from college, which side of the IT industry are they drawn to, and why?

When coupled with the back-office focus that has dominated the history of Enterprise IT, this voluntary career-track separation helps explain the pattern shown in the figure. Enterprise IT is often characterized as a 'Land of No' – at various times telling its organization: no personal computers, no local area networks, no iPhones, no Facebook, no Dropbox, and so on, only to change these views over time.

In many ways this caution has been understandable – if mostly on the wrong side of history. Given its mission, Enterprise IT was understandably wary and risk-averse. However, as digital technologies become strategic to the very core of the firm, more entrepreneurial and supply-side cultures are becoming a requirement. Unfortunately, in many organizations, the bulk of IT staff still find it hard to make the transition from *technology service providers* to *digital business leaders*, and this often undermines their effectiveness.

As shown on the next page, this mindset challenge starts with the CIO.

What type of CIO does your organization have?

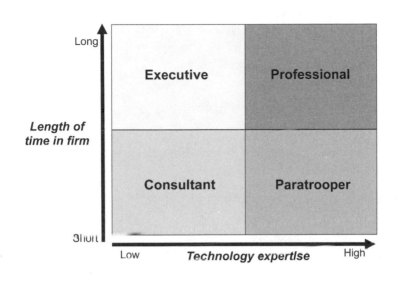

The IT industry has debated the future of the Chief Information Officer for literally decades. Should this person be the Chief Digital Officer of the firm, or is the role more about providing effective internal IT services? Is the CIO a full member of the executive team, or does he or she have a lesser status, perhaps reporting to the CFO?

For many years, we have used the figure above to assess these issues. The x-axis indicates the technical depth of the CIO, while the y-axis depicts the CIO's length of time in his or her current organization. These dimensions categorize the four *CIO role types* below:

1. **Professional CIOs** have a strong technical background, and have been with their firm for many years. They are a known entity across the organization.
2. **Executive CIOs** have broad experience within their organization and are respected for their managerial abilities, but they lack technical depth, and thus often need to earn the confidence of IT.
3. **Paratrooper CIOs** have strong technical skills, but tend not to stay in any one organization for long. They are often brought in to shake things up.
4. **Consultant CIOs** tend to be brought in for their outside-in perspective as a digital strategist, and often have a consulting or professional services background.

Each of these roles creates very different leadership and decision-making dynamics, while also shaping the answers to the assessment questions that follow.

Digital leadership assessment: Enterprise IT

	Disagree				Agree
	1	2	3	4	5
1. Enterprise IT has kept up with new social, mobile, cloud, and machine intelligence technologies	☐	☐	☐	☐	☐
2. Enterprise IT can rapidly develop, test, and deploy new digital capabilities	☐	☐	☐	☐	☐
3. Enterprise IT works well with key business delivery functions	☐	☐	☐	☐	☐
4. Back-office systems are well integrated with new market-facing applications	☐	☐	☐	☐	☐
5. Enterprise IT provides important digital business leadership	☐	☐	☐	☐	☐

In the end, the way Enterprise (or Central) IT is seen is mostly influenced by its ability to deliver. Have there been visible successes or failures? Does the IT organization meet its deadlines? Is it responsive to the changing needs of the firm?

But perceptions are also critical. It's not always easy to know what 'good' looks like, how much IT projects should cost, or whether competitors do things better or worse. Yet these uncertainties don't stop people from having strong opinions. The questions above typically shape these perceptions, as expanded upon below:

1. It's critical that Enterprise IT embraces new ways of working as they arise and gain market momentum, rather than instinctively resisting them.
2. Enterprise IT needs to be seen as being able to move quickly, perhaps through team-based agile methods, as opposed to traditional waterfall methodologies.
3. Ideally, people all across the organization should enjoy working with and learning from Enterprise IT, as opposed to feeling out of sync or at odds.
4. It helps a lot if people can see that existing back-office systems are evolving and becoming more like the web and app experiences they use in their personal lives.
5. Perhaps the bottom-line test is whether the rest of the firm looks to Enterprise IT first for new digital ideas and solutions, or only when really necessary.

These issues will be discussed more deeply in the next chapter, on the future of the IT organization.

A quick entrepreneurial leadership and culture check

1. Would you give $10 million to a bunch of twenty-somethings who want to try to transform your core operational processes?

2. Can you sustain support for new digital initiatives, even at the expense of short-term profitability?

3. Are you comfortable hiring people more digitally savvy than you, even if they might challenge your leadership position in the firm?

4. Can your firm experiment, fail fast, and learn? Or are failures mostly hidden and/or punished?

5. Is your firm all-in on a digital future, or mostly hedging its bets?

The deliberately provocative questions in the figure above show why digital leadership is likely to continue to be mostly provided by supply side forces. In traditional firms, the answers to the questions above are generally 'No':

1. A venture capitalist can be very successful if nine investments fail and one hits it big. Most incumbent firms simply can't work this way.
2. Executive incentives and external financial market pressures drive companies to emphasize short-term profitability.
3. Many executives with a non-technical background are understandably wary of hiring powerful digital leaders whom they cannot easily control.
4. While companies often talk about the need to learn by failing fast, in most organizations, good news is trumpeted and bad news is buried or punished.
5. Perhaps the biggest difference between start-ups and incumbents is that the former are fully committed to taking a chance on something new, while the latter typically prefer to wait for more evidence.

For these reasons, Matrix firms will continue to have the edge in many emerging technology areas. While incumbents have many advantages in size, resources, brands, expertise, and other domains, digitally they are often in a defensive mode. Fortunately for incumbents, this caution is more of a problem in some industry sectors than others, and there is often plenty of room for both new and existing market participants.

A leadership agenda for digital transformation

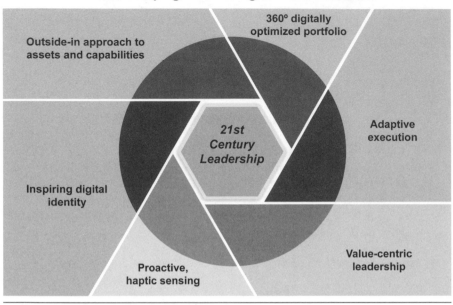

We summarize this chapter with the figure above, which brings together the challenges traditional large organizations face as they seek to become more digital and modernize themselves for the 21st century.   We advise readers to task their leadership teams to:

- **Find an inspiring digital identity.**   Only by knowing who it is digitally can an organization motivate employees and sustain the required focus and ecosystem fit.
- **Sustain proactive, *haptic* sensing.**   Keep aware of and develop a hands-on feel for important industry, technology, marketplace, and security developments.
- **Take an outside-in approach.**   As discussed throughout this book, companies need to look first to the Matrix and the external world for innovation, skills, and ideas.
- **Pursue 360-degree optimization.**   This means applying digital technologies, as well as human and machine learning, across the full operational stack.
- **Be able to adapt.**   The technology world will always have its surprises, and the speed with which firms can change and execute is often a critical differentiator.
- **Lead through value.**   In the end, leadership is about sensing when the risk/ reward equation turns favorable, and convincing others to follow along.

Taken together, these six areas can define a practical digital leadership agenda. But to pursue this agenda, all the members of the team – executives, employees, partners, and Enterprise IT – must play a role. Digital leadership will remain a team sport.

Chapter 8
The future of Enterprise IT

In this chapter

- The role of Enterprise IT is constantly evolving
- Like CEOs/COOs/CFOs, CIOs must have a 360-degree view
- The perennial Enterprise IT challenge
- Companies tend to have a consistent culture of IT adoption
- How will the Matrix change the traditional sourcing view of IT?
- Expect the traditional *4P* roles of Enterprise IT to continue
  1. *Provide* solid, effective, and modern IT services
  2. *Promote* a strong technology vision for the organization
  3. *Partner* effectively with marketing, product IT, and the ecosystem
  4. Think like a C-suite *Peer*
- Most IT organizations have a challenging journey ahead
- Don't let the legacy put your company at risk

*In this chapter, we will look at the evolution of the IT organization thus far and identify its key '4P' roles: as service **Providers**, technology **Promoters**, business **Partners**, and strategic **Peers**. We will then discuss how each of these roles will evolve in today's outside-in, Matrix-driven marketplace, ideally leading to a revitalized, front-of-the-firm Enterprise IT function.*

The role of Enterprise IT is constantly evolving

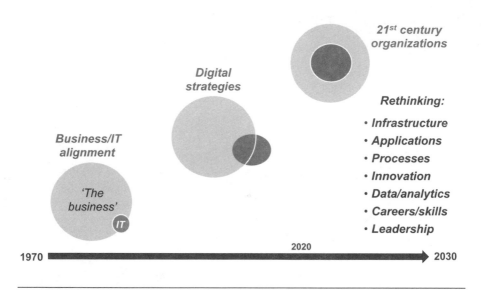

The name has steadily evolved through the years – from the Data Processing department, to the Management Information Systems organization, and today Central IT, the IT organization, or (the term we prefer) *Enterprise IT*. And right from the start, people have speculated about its future. In the 1960s and 70s, corporate IT seemed an alien world, consisting of separate people, speaking a separate language, typically located in a separate building. IT people even referred to the rest of the company as 'the business.' What did that make Enterprise IT: 'the non-business'?

Of course, as the years have gone by, the mystery of digital technology has steadily eroded. But this growing familiarity has only spawned additional questions. What IT work should be done by employees and business units, and what should be done by Enterprise IT? How much should organizations spend on technology? Who is ultimately responsible for our digital strategies? What is it reasonable to expect?

The increase in familiarity with information technology has coincided with its growing pervasiveness in large organizations, and this pervasiveness is just getting started. As suggested by the figure above, technology will increasingly underlie just about every business operation, and this will require organizations to *rethink* virtually every aspect of the firm. As businesses are increasingly defined by their software designs, information flows, and digital platforms, business and IT will become ever-more inseparable.

Like CEOs/COOs/CFOs, CIOs must have a 360-degree view

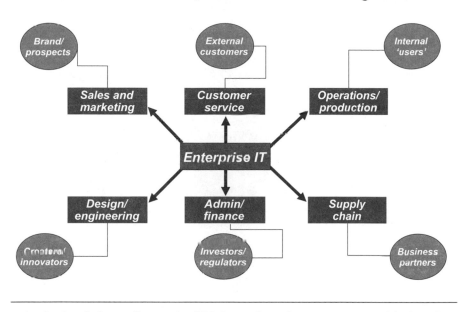

As depicted above, Enterprise IT is best viewed as a corporate-wide function, touching upon every major aspect of the firm, and thus, like CEOs, COOs, and CFOs (and HR), CIOs need to develop 360-degree perspective. But historically, their perspective has been mostly *inside-out*. IT has tended to see the internal constituencies shown above as its 'customers,' or 'users,' and has often not had the resources to fully engage with the external world as well.

In this sense, the IT function resembles Finance and HR, which also spend most of their time and energy on internal challenges. In IT's case, these internal tendencies are compounded by the intense, heads-down individual focus that many IT activities – such as systems analysis and software development – require. But this inside-out dynamic is becoming increasingly problematic. As discussed throughout this book, IT leaders need to see and respond to the digital Matrix that is surrounding them, and this requires much more of an outward-looking mindset. Too many IT organizations are at risk of slowing their firms down.

Additionally, the boundaries between sales, marketing, customer service, and other functional units aren't nearly as distinct as the organizational chart above might imply. And while somewhat-arbitrary functional boundaries don't necessarily change the way that Finance or HR operate, cross-system business processes and information integration are critical parts of the Enterprise IT mission, and this reinforces the complex inside-out demands described above.

The perennial Enterprise IT challenge

Value through back-office provision (COO/CFO)	*Value through front-of-the-firm digital leadership (CEO/CMO)*
• Inside-out	• Outside-in
• Cost efficiency	• Business impact
• Standardization	• New ways of working
• Secure/compliant	• Agent of change
• IT budgets	• Digital business

We have long used the metaphor of the two-headed Janus to describe the challenges faced by Enterprise IT organizations. Janus was an ancient Roman god, believed to be able to see equally clearly into the past and the future. We think this is an apt description of what IT organizations are asked to do every day. For example:

- Enterprise IT needs to make sure that its systems meet the demands listed on the left side of the figure, and in this sense its objectives are closely aligned with those of the typical COO/CFO.
- But the IT industry itself is mostly about the future and the new possibilities that technology can enable. The CEO/CMO agenda is usually much more about what can be done on the right side of the figure.

Every firm seeks to strike a balance between these two missions. From our experience, if IT organizations are spending two-thirds of their energy on the left and one-third on the right, they are probably in good shape. But, unfortunately, there are quite a few organizations where the balance is closer to nine-tenths/one-tenth, and such back-office IT organizations can never keep up with the expectations of their firm and marketplace. In these cases, Enterprise IT isn't represented in the board room; digital leadership tends to come from other parts of the organization, and IT is often subject to relentless cost-cutting and/or large-scale outsourcing.

Companies tend to have a consistent culture of IT adoption

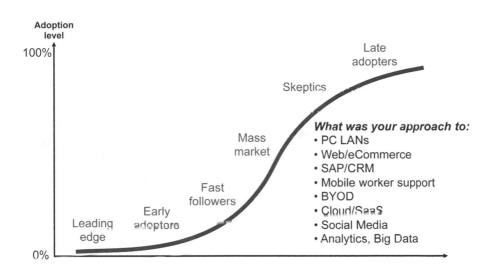

While the previous figure presented a binary model that sharply contrasts internal and external IT priorities, the real world is obviously more nuanced. Different companies have different IT strategies and needs, and this is naturally reflected in their attitudes toward technology adoption.

Indeed, the pattern in most industries looks like the familiar S-curve shown above. Not every player can be (or wants to be) at the *leading edge*, or even a *fast follower*. At some point, successful technologies reach their *mass-market* phase, and, of course, there are always *skeptics*. As we noted in Chapter 3, although we constantly hear that the rate of technology adoption is accelerating, the evidence shows a more stable situation.

When we show this S-curve to clients, many say that they see themselves as fast followers, believing that this is the 'sweet spot' in the market in terms of both minimizing risk, and maximizing gains. Of course, by definition, not everyone can be a fast follower, but the goal is understandable.

While all of this may seem like common sense, what is interesting to us is that company attitudes tend to be consistent both over time and across different technology types. Organizations tend to have a relatively fixed technology adoption culture, and this makes their future behavior more predictable as we start to think about the eventual adoption of IoT, 3D printing, biometrics, machine intelligence, serverless architectures, etc.

How will the Matrix change the traditional sourcing view of IT?

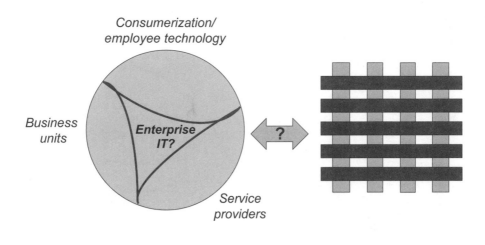

Thus far, we have discussed the evolution and expansion of the Enterprise IT function over time, the need for IT leadership to take a 360-degree view of their organization, and the competition between inside-out and outside-in possibilities and demands.

But the key question of this chapter is how the emergence of a full-blown digital Matrix might change these dynamics. The figure above looks at this question from a sourcing perspective. Businesses have traditionally had three main alternatives to their Enterprise IT:

- Expect employees to do more things for themselves in terms of devices, apps, internet usage, and related activities.
- Make business units responsible for their own IT applications, in order to keep work closer to the customer and reduce the potential for finger-pointing.
- Contract with third-party IT services firms in selected areas, to leverage their talent, experience, and scale of operations.

While theoretically these three options could all but eliminate the need for a central IT organization, reality has proven otherwise, as ever-expanding business needs continue to require significant internal resources. More fundamentally, the Matrix is about much more than sourcing, since with many Matrix capabilities there will be no viable internal alternative. To think through the implications of this shift, we need to look more closely at the various roles that Enterprise IT currently plays and assess how they are likely to evolve.

Expect the traditional *4P* roles of Enterprise IT to continue

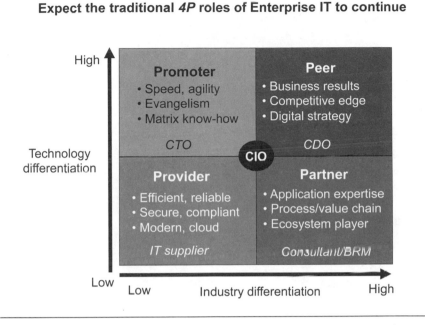

The figure above has long been our core diagram for describing the role(s) that Enterprise IT can play in a large organization. The diagram is based on the belief that Enterprise IT can provide competitive advantage in two main ways: it can be better technically (y-axis); or it can better apply technology to its industry (x-axis). These classifications lead to four possible roles:

- **Providers** serve largely as suppliers of agreed-upon technology services.
- **Promoters** evangelize for the use of new technologies in the firm.
- **Partners** emphasize working closely with key business units by establishing strong business relationship management (BRM).
- **Peers** are full members of the C-suite and drive the firm's digital strategy.

While every IT organization – and every CIO – plays all of these *4P* roles to at least some extent, one role is usually dominant. Additionally, while each role requires different skills, behaviors, and metrics, each one also tends to build upon the others. For example, unless one is a reliable Provider, it's difficult to expand into any of the other three roles. Similarly, Peers need a strong grounding in all of the other three areas.

We believe that each of these 4P roles will continue to be relevant through the Matrix era, and thus the Enterprise IT function isn't going away. However, today's powerful outside-in forces will significantly transform each role. We'll discuss each one in turn.

Provide solid, effective, and modern IT services

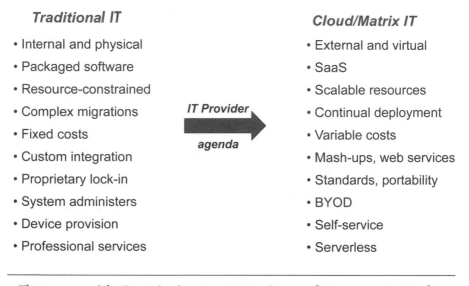

Traditional IT

- Internal and physical
- Packaged software
- Resource-constrained
- Complex migrations
- Fixed costs
- Custom integration
- Proprietary lock-in
- System administers
- Device provision
- Professional services

IT Provider

agenda

Cloud/Matrix IT

- External and virtual
- SaaS
- Scalable resources
- Continual deployment
- Variable costs
- Mash-ups, web services
- Standards, portability
- BYOD
- Self-service
- Serverless

The essence of the Provider function is to make sure that an organization has a solid, reliable, efficient, agile, compliant, and secure digital infrastructure. While definitions of *infrastructure* can be narrow (servers, networks, devices, email) or broad (key applications and processes), it is generally seen as the shared operating environment of the firm. No Enterprise IT organization can succeed without being effective in this role, the nature of which is changing significantly.

As suggested by the figure, the differences between the traditional use of the word 'cloud' and our use of the word 'Matrix' in this area aren't particularly significant. In both cases, we are talking about the shift from dedicated internal resources to more virtual, external, and variable capabilities, and the many benefits that can come with this approach. However, it isn't easy to get the timing and extent of these changes right, and as noted in Chapter 5, many production and legacy systems will stay inside the firm for the foreseeable future.

Looking ahead, the Provider role will continue to shift from being mostly a builder to mostly a buyer. There will be less need for internal staff to spend time on employee devices and basic network and messaging services; these will be either consumerized (BYOD) or delivered by suppliers. Although becoming an effective Provider requires embracing these changes, not resisting them, many IT organizations struggle to overcome the internal mindset built up over the years.

Promote a strong technology vision for the organization

1. How is the technology landscape changing?

2. How can new technologies make us more agile and productive?

3. How can we go from concept to scale more quickly?

4. What technical skills and talent do we need, and not need?

5. When and how should we leverage open source approaches?

6. Which vendors and partners should we embrace, and avoid?

7. How can we leverage and contribute to the Matrix?

8. What should our architectural roadmap look like going forward?

The CTO agenda

For most of the 21st century, the Enterprise IT organizations we work with have been largely focused on making the shift from the Provider to the Partner model, in which the role of technology and even that of the Chief Technology Officer is somewhat diminished. The emphasis has been much more on business results than aggressive technology adoption.

But in recent years, the need for greater technological sophistication has risen, and with it the Promoter role. Taking advantage of the coming wave of innovation – machine intelligence, IoT, biometrics, 3D printing, chatbots, 5G, DevOps, mobile payments, location awareness, and so on – will often require deep technical and architectural understanding, as well as the ability to attract and manage the corresponding talent.

To thrive in this future, large organizations need people with native cloud skills, who are used to working in the open source world, who keep up with the latest software tools and languages, and who are comfortable being part of agile, multi-function teams in uncertain and fast-changing circumstances, all while maintaining architectural clarity and integrity. Not surprisingly, many IT organizations – already under a budget and resource squeeze – are struggling with these challenges.

But to effectively address the questions in the figure, companies shouldn't rely entirely on their suppliers. They need strong technology leadership and a vigorous CTO function, willing and able to promote a digital vision for the firm, while making it clear what skills and capabilities the organization needs to succeed.

***Partner* effectively with marketing, product IT, and the ecosystem**

Marketing partnerships

- User interfaces/experience
- Mobile/location
- Payments/Bitcoin
- Internet ad serving
- Web, eCommerce
- Customer support
- Analytics, Big Data
- Privacy/permissions
- Search engine optimization
- Right to forget
- Agents/bots
- Machine intelligence

The Partner

BRM agenda

Product/engineering partnerships

- General-purpose technologies
- Programming/development
- User interfaces, experience
- Cloud/SaaS architectures
- Serverless architectures
- Customer service integration
- Project management
- Mobility, web, IoT
- Analytics, Big Data, AI/MI
- Documentation
- Discovery/archiving
- Security/compliance

As noted earlier, in recent years the strategy of most Enterprise IT organizations has been to become a more effective business partner. Often this has been viewed primarily as a *soft skill* challenge. IT professionals have been challenged to improve their business knowledge, communication and negotiation skills, their personal confidence and power, and even the way they look, dress, and appear. Improved business/IT partnerships are now particularly important in two areas:

- Marketing has shifted from a low-tech profession – mass-media advertising, focus groups, collateral, etc. – to a high-tech one. Today, the boundaries between what is digital marketing and what is IT are often subjective, and unless the marketing/IT partnership is strong, problems will arise. Many firms have had to work hard on this relationship.
- Engineering and embedded *product IT* are becoming increasingly important in today's connected world. Traditionally, Enterprise IT has mostly had an arm's-length relationship with these groups. But as shown in the figure, the boundaries between engineering and IT are also blurring, as many of the same skills are now required, especially in a smart-product, IoT, and architectural context.

Looking ahead, external partnerships will become the third big Partner challenge in areas such as ecosystem cooperation, B2B negotiations, APIs and standards, defining the customer experience, sharing data, leveraging platform and network effects, fine-tuning business models, and assessing the associated risks. Most IT organizations are not fully prepared for these challenges.

Think like a C-suite *Peer*

1. How is technology changing our business environment?
2. What is our firm's digital strategy, identity, and vision?
3. How can we establish a platform business model?
4. Can technology give us a sustainable competitive advantage?
5. Is this merger, acquisition, or divestment a good idea?
6. How is technology affecting our share price and brand?
7. What are our most valuable information assets?
8. Who should we choose as critical ecosystem partners?
9. What are the biggest technology risks we face?
10. Does our firm have the skills, talent, and culture it needs?

The CDO agenda

As discussed in the previous chapter on digital leadership, in many companies there is an ongoing drama in the C-suite. Regardless of whether the CDO title is used or not, who, if anyone, best speaks to the strategic questions listed in the figure above?

Importantly, Enterprise IT can't jump directly from the Provider to the Peer roles; it needs a reputation for success as both a Promoter and Partner. As the Group CIO of a global insurance company recently told us:

"My IT leadership team and I now have an outstanding reputation for globalization, rationalization, and cost reduction. By and large, projects deliver on their promises, on time, in full. For the most part, the business agrees. But here's the crunch: while we are now known for efficiency and delivery, Enterprise IT is far from having a reputation for agility, business innovation, or growth. Yet that is where all of today's digital action is. So, unfortunately, I am not the obvious or even the leading candidate to drive our digital agenda in the coming years."

This quote captures the need to shift from inside-out to outside-in thinking, the imbalances of our Janus model, and the importance of each of our 4P roles. It also shows the distance that many IT organizations must travel if they want to be seen as true business Peers, as discussed further on the next page.

Most IT organizations have a challenging journey ahead

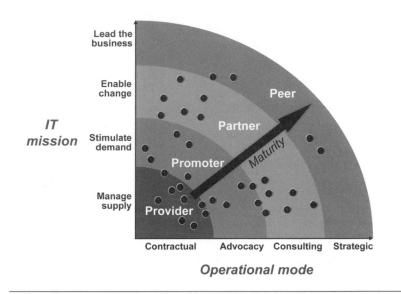

Operational mode

While it is natural to see the shift from Provider to Peer as an inevitable maturity journey, reality shows otherwise. The data points in the figure reflect our sense of the actual position of some of the large organizations we work with. The picture makes it clear that there is no overall trend or direction, however much we wish that there were.

To us, the most striking aspect of the figure is how few IT organizations are true business Peers. The vast majority are spread across the other three roles. This leads us to the following conclusions about the likely evolution of Enterprise IT:

- IT organizations that are still at the Provider stage will tend to face a shrinking future, as suppliers provide many basic services, and advanced digital work and leadership take place elsewhere in the organization.
- Those in the Promoter stage will need a strong and vocal CTO function to keep pace with fast-moving front-of-the-firm market requirements. But finding the right person will often be challenging.
- Those that are positioned as business Partners will need to embrace a much more outside-in and ecosystem-oriented approach.
- While the CDO/Peer role will flourish (in effect if not always in name), many of these leaders will come from outside of traditional IT.

In short, IT organizations aren't going away, but their futures will be increasingly defined by the digital Matrix that surrounds them.

Don't let the IT legacy put your company at risk

Which of these best describes your organization?

1. Our legacy systems will mostly remain as they are, and we believe that this strategy does not pose a significant business risk

2. Our legacy systems will remain largely as they are, but we need to monitor this closely as this represents a potentially significant business risk

3. We are modernizing our legacy systems through cloud migration, wrappers, containers, or other technology approaches

4. We are re-writing many key legacy applications, and are willing to essentially write off older system investments

5. Other _____

Few IT questions are more important than what to do about so-called *legacy* systems. These are older applications, often developed decades ago, typically for mainframe computers. Many of these systems – in banks, insurance companies, airlines, utilities, governments, and elsewhere – are still vital production environments, but are not well suited to today's emerging digital world. As older workers retire, just retaining people who can use older programming languages and understand how these systems work can be a major challenge.

Many of the world's largest firms are now wrestling with the questions above, which can reach 'bet-the-company' importance. While we know of organizations following each of the paths shown, no matter which path is chosen, all of our *4P* roles should come into play. Providers need to make sure that critical services are not interrupted. Partners need to clearly explain legacy system implications to the rest of the organization. Promoters need to recommend the best technical options, while Peers must be the lead voice as to what, if anything, should be done.

Businesses can't afford to get their legacy management wrong, yet most firms are in a classic sleepwalking situation. While the costs of pursuing options three and four tend to be large and immediate, the downsides of options one and two often accumulate relatively slowly over time. This is a formula for short-term inaction. Most traditional firms are still in the midst of this dilemma, for which there are no easy answers.

Chapter 9

Digital as a career requirement

In this chapter

- We can't have a digital future without digital people
- Traditional work/life boundaries are eroding
- Digital innovation is now shifting to the 'human platform'
- As with machine intelligence, there is a high 'creep' factor
- The Matrix sees and tracks the 'virtual you'
- Thriving in this world requires a strong digital foundation
- Maintaining a strong foundation requires continual learning
- Ongoing learning stems from a digital commitment and mindset
- Work and consumer IT skills are increasingly the same
- Career success is still the main motivator for changing habits
- Confidence comes from embracing digital
- Anxiety comes from resisting digital
- A 'digital mindstack' approach to personal development
- The social media mindstack: Where do you want to play?
- Are you preparing for a 21st century career?

In this chapter, we will describe how innovation is shifting to 'the human platform,' how the walls between working and living are blurring, and how the Matrix supports and leverages these activities by seeing the entire 'virtual you.' We will then discuss the implications of these changes for our digital skills and learning, their impact on our careers, habits, and preferences, and the digital mindset needed to maximize our individual 21st century possibilities.

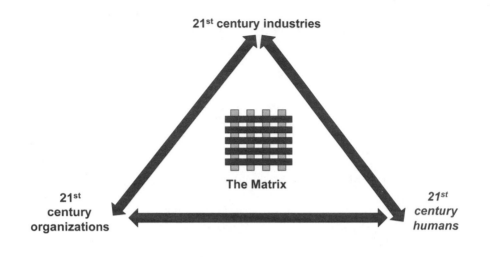

We can't have a digital future without digital people

21st century industries

The Matrix

21st century organizations

21st century humans

Thus far, we have seen how the Matrix is changing how *industries* innovate, operate, and compete, while challenging the traditional boundaries between what happens inside vs. outside of an *organization*.

In this chapter, we will assess the third leg of the *triple transformation*: what the Matrix means to us as *individuals*. The way each of us innovates, operates, and competes is also changing, while the lines between work and home, and leisure and learning, are eroding. As in the business world, there are fantastic opportunities ahead, but individual skills and careers will be disrupted too.

We live in an increasingly competitive global economy where many forms of work can be done almost anywhere, and where machine intelligence and automation are becoming ever-more capable. These profound changes are creating new possibilities, but also new anxieties. Maximizing the former while minimizing the latter is a good working definition of what it means to become a *21st century human* (21CH).

We use the term 21CH with the full awareness that some readers might be put off by the implied assertion that *going digital* is now some type of essential human requirement. We agree this is far from the case. But we would argue strongly that those who get on the upside of the technology adoption curve will, on average, fare much better than those who do not. The digital world we envision needs sufficiently digital people, both culturally and technically, as explained throughout this chapter.

Traditional work/life boundaries are eroding

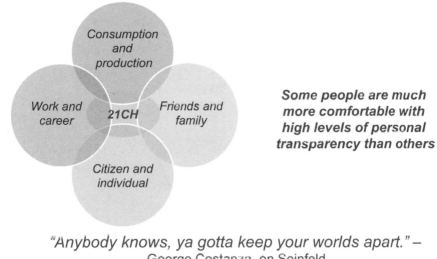

Consumption and production

Work and career

21CH

Friends and family

Citizen and individual

Some people are much more comfortable with high levels of personal transparency than others

"Anybody knows, ya gotta keep your worlds apart." –
George Costanza, on Seinfeld
See https://www.youtube.com/watch?v=NBZVaNpwub8

The figure above shows how the boundaries between working and living are eroding. Whereas personal computer and internet usage was once indeed *personal,* even anonymous, social media is putting much more of the *full human* on display.

For example, children can go to LinkedIn and review their parents' entire careers, as well as the overall way they present themselves, once areas of great mystery. Similarly, in most workplaces there has long been an expectation that we should check our politics at the company door. But, of course, on Twitter and Facebook, many citizens freely air their views – be they on Brexit, Trump, terrorism, or other controversial topics.

There really is no 'company door,' and nowhere to hide anymore. But as suggested by the famous quote from the US sitcom *Seinfeld,* some people are much less comfortable with these colliding worlds than others. Indeed, while social media has enabled a great many important innovations, the expectation that we will expose our full selves to everyone represents a major psychological and cultural shift, whose end effects are still far from clear. An eventual backlash is certainly possible.

But overall, the Matrix will drive even greater transparency. While we can try to maintain separate work and personal identities, our biometrics are the same whether we are in work, consumer, friends, family, or citizenship mode. The Matrix can literally see the *whole you,* as explained further on the following pages.

Digital innovation is now shifting to the *human platform*

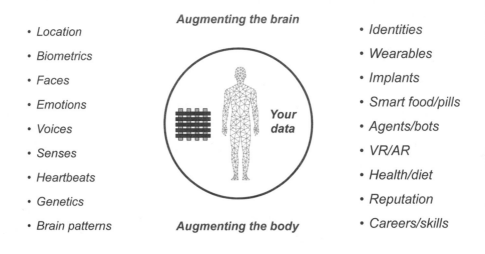

- Location
- Biometrics
- Faces
- Emotions
- Voices
- Senses
- Heartbeats
- Genetics
- Brain patterns

Augmenting the brain

Your data

Augmenting the body

- Identities
- Wearables
- Implants
- Smart food/pills
- Agents/bots
- VR/AR
- Health/diet
- Reputation
- Careers/skills

While colliding worlds characterized the first phase of 21CH transformation, the next phase will be much more about data and technology. Over the course of the 2020s, it will become clear that the center of digital innovation has shifted to the human platform.

Of course, digital technology will continue to get smaller and more powerful. Looking back, each generation of IT miniaturization – mainframes, PCs, smartphones – has created major new markets and possibilities, while increasing the number of devices and data volumes by at least an order of magnitude. This pattern seems highly likely to repeat itself.

As shown in the figure, the Matrix will be used to augment both our brains and our bodies. Already today, deep learning, analytics, and the internet of things are drawing insights from how we walk and talk, the rhythms of our breathing and heartbeats, the patterns of our thinking and emotions, and our unique faces, eyes, and genetics, while enhancing our capabilities through wearables, implants, and the nutrients we consume.

But these innovations are just beginning. Digital technology will merge with healthcare, fitness, diet, medicine, genetics, entertainment, aging, and increasingly with our five senses, greatly expanding the way we think about what humans can do. As we saw in Chapter 3, major new technology eras are almost always led by new players, so we should fully expect a new generation of suppliers, including those from China, to lead in many of these human platform areas.

As with machine intelligence, there is a high 'creep' factor

1. Would you want computers to recognize you based on your face, voice, or gait?

2. Would you take an fMRI brain scan to prove that you are telling the truth?

3. Would you implant a chip in your hand to replace all of your keys?

4. Would you wear a watch that identified any changes in your heartbeat patterns?

5. Would you eat synthetic nutrients to either save time or increase performance?

6. Would you let a deep learning system look at you and predict your life expectancy?

7. Would you want to pay insurance prices based on your driving, diet, etc.?

8. Would you use technology to greatly improve your memory, seeing, or hearing?

9. Do you really want to know all of your genetic tendencies, and probabilities?

10. Are you willing to let VR and robotics be part of your sex life?

While there are many exciting possibilities, the innovations on the previous page often elicit the same sort of *'creep' factor* that we saw with machine intelligence. What we broadly label *biohacking* – implants, supplements, VR/AR, wearables, genetic manipulation, technology-to-brain interfaces, etc. – clearly makes many people uncomfortable. Most of us aren't ready for the types of questions shown above.

But we often over-estimate society's resistance to change. Consider that today, we routinely supplement our teeth with fillings, braces, crowns, and implants; our eyes with glasses and contacts; and our hearing with electronics. We seek to improve our appearance through cosmetic surgery, Botox treatments, liposuction, and tattoos, just as we try to enhance our performance with Adderall, HGH, and other boosters. While some of these treatments work better – and are more socially acceptable – than others, the evidence suggests that people will not just accept digital enhancements, but will demand them, once they see the cost/benefit equation turn favorable.

As with VCRs, cable TV, and the internet, pornography will be an important early adoption driver. But soldiers, athletes, and celebrities, as well as the aging, infirm, and disabled, will also drive demand, as they will tend to reap the most direct benefits. Perhaps the biggest unanswered question is whether the youths of the future will embrace or resist the possibilities listed in the figure. Will they be seen as cool? In which countries?

The Matrix sees and tracks the 'virtual you'

Work and career	Consumption and production	Citizen and individual	Identity and biometrics
• Job/position	• Purchases	• Education	• Age/gender
• Credentials	• Needs	• Activities	• Height/weight
• Experience	• Ad views	• Hobbies	• Health
• Skills	• Sales	• Interests	• Fitness/BMI
• Languages	• Reviews	• Orientation	• Face/eyes
• Postings	• Ratings	• Causes	• Fingerprints
• Profiles	• Likes	• Politics	• Voice
• Awards	• Postings	• Beliefs	• Gait/posture
• Connections	• Communities	• Tastes	• Hair/skin color
• Influence	• Connections	• Families	• Sleep patterns
• Reputation	• Sharing	• Friends	• Genetics
• Endorsements	• Gigs	• Emotions	• Ancestry
• Associations	• Sentiments	• Attitudes	• Implants
• Communities ...	• Used markets ...	• Charities ...	• Brain patterns ...
• Your success	• Your commerce	• Your interests	• Your biology

One of the reasons that the term 'the cloud' feels increasingly archaic is that its underlying metaphor implies a technology environment that is 'out there' somewhere. Clouds are in the sky, and thus not directly connected to people down on earth.

But the reality is that we are constantly connected to the Matrix, and this steady flow of individual information is an essential source of its value, as shown by the vast range of personal data listed in the figure. Taken together, the four categories above provide a comprehensive picture of our individual activity, and suggest the wider sense of the terms *virtual you* and *quantified self*. Indeed, the Matrix will know us and predict us much better than any one company – and in some ways better than we know ourselves.

Of course, all of this personal data inevitably raises concerns about privacy, misuse, media manipulation, and potentially coercive social control, and no doubt there will be unauthorized and abusive practices. However, similar Big Brother worries have come at every stage of IT industry progress. So, although there will be heated debates in areas such as the *right to forget* and trans-border data flows, and controversial new forms of marketing as well as government projects such as China's Social Credit System, we believe these issues will mostly prove manageable, especially if customers can supplement today's *your-data-for-our-services* business model with the increasing ability to control and monetize their own information.

Thriving in this world requires a strong digital foundation

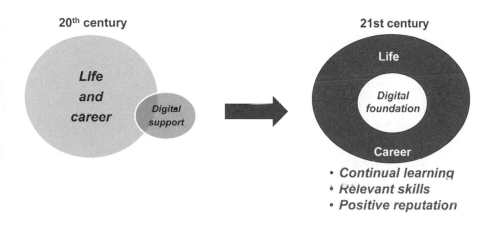

In Chapter 2, we stressed how businesses need to be grounded in a solid *data foundation* to leverage machine intelligence. The same is true for us as individuals. As shown in the figure, we see a shift from one where digital usage was an extension of our lives and careers, to one where it is much more central. We say this for two main reasons. First, employee IT usage is shifting from personal productivity to more job-specific and collaborative tasks. People who master modern technologies are often much more productive than those less skilled. It can be a huge career advantage.

More subtly, there is the greatly increased importance of our *digital reputations*. Like it or not, our virtual reputations are often at least as important as our reputations in the physical world – for the simple reason that so many more people know us only through our virtual selves. This is why so many people feel the need to curate their LinkedIn, Twitter, Facebook, Uber, OpenTable, and other digital reputations, even though to many people, young and old, this can create stress and anxiety.

For better or worse, the virtual world increasingly expects us to serve as our own PR agents. It's another fundamental and yet often uncomfortable psychological shift that often determines who fully embraces modern social platforms and who doesn't. Today, each of us must decide how much we want to give and take from the digital world.

Maintaining a strong foundation requires continual learning

1980 - 2005

- DOS commands and files
- WP, spreadsheets, graphics
- Printers, peripherals
- Modems, datacom
- Back-up/recovery
- GUIs and browsers
- ISPs, broadband
- eCommerce, email
- Music and photo management
- Communities, wikis
- RSS, feeds, blogs
- Passwords/security ...

+

Hands-on learning and experience

2005 - 2030

- Mobility, apps, location
- Social media services
- WiFi, Skype, Bluetooth
- Videos, podcasts, cameras
- Collaboration, APIs, IFTTT
- Data, privacy, analytics
- Biometrics, authentication
- IoT, wearables, implants
- Hacking, making, 3DP
- Virtual, augmented, 3D
- Brain, genetic patterns
- Agents, bots, avatars ...

The left side of the figure above shows just how much digital learning most of us have already done. Individuals who have excelled in these areas have reaped significant rewards, especially in the workplace, where the level of such skills still varies widely.

But the list on the right-hand side should make it clear that today's technologies are both much more powerful and much more personal in nature. Of course, many of these capabilities are still in their early stages, and thus are not essential for everyone to engage with today, but by the 2030 end-point shown, these – and many other capabilities not yet known – will surely be broad-based societal forces.

In both the left- and right-side columns, the best way to learn about new technologies has been by direct experience, as opposed to more classroom- or book-based approaches. While there was once a significant industry ready to help us learn to use personal computers, this approach has all but vanished, as self-teaching and online assistance have taken hold, and as supply-side innovations such as graphical interfaces and touch screens have made using technology simpler and more intuitive.

But we shouldn't kid ourselves; learning new technologies can still be difficult and time-consuming, with the benefits often more down-the-road than immediate. This is why personal belief and commitment are so important, as discussed on the following pages.

Ongoing learning stems from a digital commitment and mindset

Resisting this story ➡️ **Embracing this story**

Resisting this story	Embracing this story
1. I don't have time	1. Technology is important to my future
2. It's not my job	2. I make time to learn new digital skills
3. I'm a technophobe	3. My online brand is as important as offline
4. This stuff doesn't matter	4. It's important that I stay informed
5. I'll just embarrass myself	5. I am what I share, on and offline
6. It's for the young	6. I have a learning and growth mindset
7. I prefer traditional media	7. The more I network, the better I do
8. I'm not a self-promoter	8. I learn by doing
9. I like my privacy	9. I see myself as a digital leader
10. I'm retiring soon	10. I embrace our increasingly digital world

---

In consulting with organizations all around the world, we've seen that attitudes toward new ways of working vary widely – from outright resistance to full-throated evangelism, as suggested by the two columns in the figure.

While it's easy to say that people should embrace the views on the right-hand side, and shun those on the left, we need to acknowledge that many highly successful people don't do this, and we shouldn't dismiss the reasons listed on the left as mere inertia, laziness, stubbornness, and / or shortsightedness. There's much more to it than that.

We group the resistance into three main camps. There is, of course, the *fear of embarrassment* – by either showing ignorance or making mistakes. Then, as we have discussed, there is also often a deep-rooted *suspicion of social technologies,* as more introverted people often view much of what happens on social media as a form of boasting. Many of these introverted people were leaders in personal computer and early internet adoption, and comprise a large share of the overall population. They often have strengths that more extroverted people lack.

Finally, there is indeed an *age* issue. As retirement approaches, many of us consciously or unconsciously calculate the risk and rewards of learning new skills, habits, and interfaces, and many can make a rational ROI case for sticking with the skills they have. The next page provides some tips for overcoming all three of these barriers.

Career success is still the main motivator for changing habits

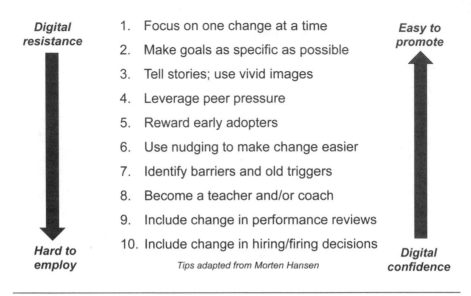

Digital resistance

Hard to employ

1. Focus on one change at a time
2. Make goals as specific as possible
3. Tell stories; use vivid images
4. Leverage peer pressure
5. Reward early adopters
6. Use nudging to make change easier
7. Identify barriers and old triggers
8. Become a teacher and/or coach
9. Include change in performance reviews
10. Include change in hiring/firing decisions

Tips adapted from Morten Hansen

Easy to promote

Digital confidence

Although many valuable skills tend to be learned first in the consumer market, the strongest motivation to *go digital* is typically career success. As shown above, we believe that the lack of digital skills will increasingly render many people hard to employ, while those with strong and double-deep skills will be much easier to promote.

But even though many people acknowledge this overall reality, they can still find it hard to change entrenched habits. The best example of this is email. While one can debate whether the failure of so many internal collaboration software initiatives is mostly a problem in software value or human learning, there's no doubt that changing people's electronic messaging habits is hard.

In a *Harvard Business Review* article in 2012, Professor Morten Hansen of UCal Berkeley recommended ten steps that organizations can take to get people to change their ways[14]. We have adapted this list to our 21st century digital purposes, as shown above.

The list is a roughly equal mix of personal tips, social/peer pressure, and performance evaluations. Of these, the social/peer effects are often the strongest, as most people don't want to feel left out. While performance reviews and hiring/firing practices obviously matter, these decisions tend to be driven primarily by whether someone is meeting their core work objectives. But when strong social pressure and real career impact are both in place, our willingness to change is greatly increased.

---

14. Morten Hansen, 'Ten Ways to Get People to Change,' *Harvard Business Review*, September 21, 2012

Work and consumer IT skills are increasingly the same

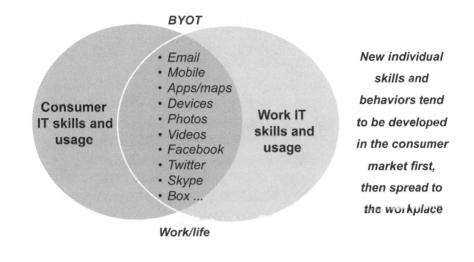

BYOT

- *Email*
- *Mobile*
- *Apps/maps*
- *Devices*
- *Photos*
- *Videos*
- *Facebook*
- *Twitter*
- *Skype*
- *Box ...*

Consumer IT skills and usage

Work IT skills and usage

New individual skills and behaviors tend to be developed in the consumer market first, then spread to the workplace

Work/life

In Part 1 of this book, we talked about the power of consumerization – the fact that consumer markets are now the center of most IT industry innovation. As shown above, consumerization clearly has important implications for individual learning and skills.

We saw this first with the Bring Your Own Device (BYOD) movement. Most people strongly prefer to use their own PCs and smartphones at work rather than a company-provided device, or awkwardly carrying both. Indeed, for many years, we have argued that we should really be talking about BYOT, with the 'T' standing for Technology, so the Bring Your Own movement covers not just devices, but technology services such as Google Docs, Dropbox, public WiFi, Facebook, Twitter, and apps. People naturally prefer to use the technologies they are most comfortable with.

These BYOT dynamics will only strengthen in the coming years. Consider the way smartphones now have recognition and authentication capabilities that far exceed traditional company token/password and other two-factor security solutions. The same will be true for speech recognition, video conferencing, and many other areas. Enterprises will increasingly want to leverage these employee-controlled capabilities.

All of this supports our overall view that those individuals who use technology actively in their personal lives will have substantial workplace advantages, as they will have the skills and confidence with which to adapt to changing work requirements. This is discussed further over the rest of this chapter.

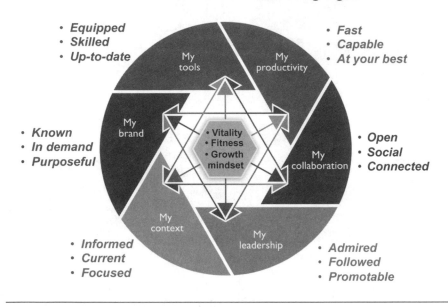

Most people want to bring their optimal self to their work, but what does this mean in a 21st century, digital context? In recent years, we have used the figure above to provide a framework with which both individuals and their organizations can assess their overall state of digital readiness. The six parts are briefly explained below:

- **Tools.** Do you have access to a modern set of hardware, software, and online services? This doesn't mean always having the latest gadgets, but it does mean using the systems and services that are and will be mainstream.
- **Productivity.** Are you seen as someone who uses technology to do things faster and/or better than average?
- **Collaboration.** Do you use technology to work effectively with people inside and outside your organization? Are you seen as connected to the right communities?
- **Information.** Do you use technology effectively to keep abreast of your field and manage the challenges of information overload?
- **Brand.** Do you have a positive online image – at work or more broadly?
- **Leadership.** Are you seen as a digital role model and a good example for others?

If the answers to these questions are mostly 'Yes,' and if you have the fitness and energy shown in the center of the figure, you are well positioned for the digital future, and will tend to have the confidence needed to explore emerging 21CH possibilities.

Anxiety comes from resisting digital

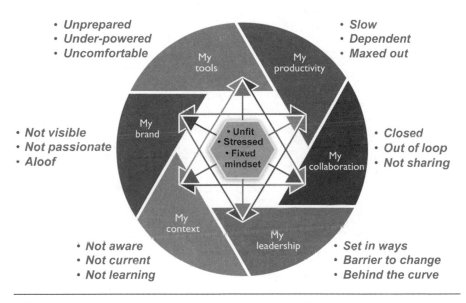

- *Unprepared*
- *Under-powered*
- *Uncomfortable*

- *Slow*
- *Dependent*
- *Maxed out*

- *Not visible*
- *Not passionate*
- *Aloof*

- *Closed*
- *Out of loop*
- *Not sharing*

- *Not aware*
- *Not current*
- *Not learning*

- *Set in ways*
- *Barrier to change*
- *Behind the curve*

While the advice on the previous page may seem like common sense, and even obvious, the reality is that many people do not fare well on such assessments. We all know colleagues who seem:

- **Under-powered.** These people use older, obsolete technologies, or (more commonly) have modern tools but really don't know how to use them effectively.
- **Maxed out.** These employees are seemingly overwhelmed by their workloads, are overly dependent upon others, or become some sort of company bottleneck.
- **Resistant.** Rather than leading change, these folks instinctively resist new ways of working, either actively or passively.
- **Closed.** For political, psychological, or other reasons, these people find sharing and transparency difficult, preferring to work mostly in their own heads.
- **Out of touch.** These colleagues don't seem to know enough about important developments, either inside or outside the organization.
- **Aloof.** People who shy away from public forums are, fairly or unfairly, often seen as detached, and not sufficiently passionate about their work.

Taken together, these dynamics can lead to a high state of anxiety that blocks learning and change, with consequences that tend to build over time. In the worst cases, they will even affect the center of the diagram – resulting in worry, stress, low energy, and sleepless nights. Unfortunately, many individuals are still on this end of the 21CH spectrum, including many who are otherwise highly productive.

A 'digital mindstack' approach to personal development

*What level do you
want to play at?**

Your purpose and meaning	*Is technology important to achieving your life's goals?*
Your sense of self	*Is technology changing how you see/assess yourself?*
Your personality and beliefs	*What motivates you? Where are your comfort zones?*
Your behavior	*Is your online style, appearance, and etiquette effective?*
Your skills and confidence	*Do you have the know-how and capabilities you need?*
Your environment	*Do you have the right IT tools, services, and workspace?*

* This six-layer stack is adapted from the work of Robert Dilts

---

While the 21st century learning challenge can be addressed by focusing directly on the topics described in the previous two pages, more psychological approaches can also be useful.   Layered models such as *neuro-linguistic programming* (also abbreviated to NLP)[15] are sometimes controversial, but they can help us see the digital skills challenge more deeply by factoring in rising levels of personal meaning.   Although the figure above should be largely self-explanatory, it can be viewed in two main parts:

- The lower three levels – environment, skills, and behavior – define your digital situation as an outsider might see it.   Is this person equipped, capable, and behaving in a way consistent with modern digital norms? We highlight 'skills' in the figure because without them the higher levels are all but impossible.

- The upper three levels are more about what is going on inside your own head: What is driving me – enthusiasm, obligation, fear? Is the way I work consistent with the way I see myself? What are my real goals and priorities in work and life, and how important is technology to them?

While there are no right and wrong answers, and clearly different people will play at very different levels, layered, psychological approaches can result in more fundamental changes than traditional coaching and training, at least for those willing to question themselves in such deeply personal ways. Not everyone is.

---

15. Robert Dilts, *Changing Belief Systems with NLP*, Meta Publications, 1990

The social media mindstack: Where do you want to play?

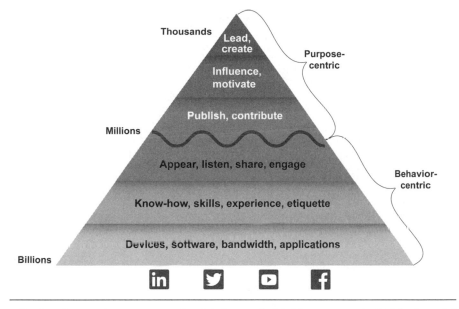

In the figure above, we apply this layered thinking to our individual social media strategies, as this remains an area of sharply different attitudes and behavior. As on the previous page, the first three levels are all about resources, skills, and behavior: Have we signed up for the mainstream social media services? Can we use them with confidence? Do we understand the etiquette in terms of how we appear, how we share, and when we engage? These skills are useful to just about everyone.

The upper levels are much more about content, meaning, and purpose: What, if anything, do we want to say – either in our own name, or under an alias? Are we trying to influence people toward a particular purpose, or are we just trying to get our own name and/or thoughts out there? Do we see ourselves as leaders in some area or cause? Why are we spending time using social media in the first place? These areas are much more personal and discretionary in nature.

As shown above, the numbers shrink rapidly as we go up the stack. Billions of people have access to modern social media, and many millions regularly engage, but the number of true leaders is far smaller. While we can certainly debate what leadership means in a world where celebrity and controversy are often richly rewarded, the key question of the model still holds: Where do you want to play, and why?

Are you preparing for a 21st century career?

		Strongly disagree 1									Strongly agree 10
1.	I am committed to having the technological know-how needed for my work	☐	☐	☐	☐	☐	☐	☐	☐	☐	☐
2.	Technology is part of my lifestyle and I leverage this experience at work	☐	☐	☐	☐	☐	☐	☐	☐	☐	☐
3.	I am a visible advocate for adopting new technology approaches	☐	☐	☐	☐	☐	☐	☐	☐	☐	☐
4.	I use new information sources effectively to keep abreast of my field	☐	☐	☐	☐	☐	☐	☐	☐	☐	☐
5.	I take my online brand and image seriously	☐	☐	☐	☐	☐	☐	☐	☐	☐	☐
6.	I consider myself to be teachable, and open to different thinking and ideas	☐	☐	☐	☐	☐	☐	☐	☐	☐	☐
7.	I believe in being transparent about my work, activities, and results	☐	☐	☐	☐	☐	☐	☐	☐	☐	☐
8.	I seek to be physically and digitally fit, and operate at my peak performance	☐	☐	☐	☐	☐	☐	☐	☐	☐	☐
9.	I am open to wearing or embedding technology to enhance my capabilities	☐	☐	☐	☐	☐	☐	☐	☐	☐	☐
10.	If a machine can do something better than me, I would embrace this progress	☐	☐	☐	☐	☐	☐	☐	☐	☐	☐

The ten questions above pull together the key themes and recommendations of this chapter, while providing an objective measurement tool.

Although individual assessments are always interesting, the true power of such exercises comes when they are done at a group or organization-wide level. Aggregate organizational measures will go a long way toward defining a company or departmental culture, while revealing differences between individuals. The most interesting results often come when an individual's self-assessment is significantly at odds with how others see them.

People naturally ask: What's a good score? While, of course, higher is generally better, what constitutes a good score will vary with the surveyed community. More information-intensive groups and businesses should have higher scores than those engaged in more physical, prescriptive, or face-to-face work, and what constitutes being *digitally savvy* varies widely across organizations and industries.

So rather than focus on the aggregate scores, we like to stress that the main goal should be to get an honest and shared consensus as to the digital culture in any one organization or group, so that if improvements are needed, there is objective guidance in terms of key areas and priorities. That said, if you are giving yourself consistently low marks, and you are in an information-driven business, you might want to consider some changes. People need to think of how their careers might play out over ten to twenty years, as the human platform era has only just begun.

Part III

Global Strategies and Competition

Chapter 10
Leveraging the technology lifecycle

In this chapter

- What's the best metaphor for business competition?
- Strategic planning is often too internal and static in nature
- Technology markets evolve in a consistent lifecycle pattern
- IT industry evolution has closely followed this pattern
- During each phase, market dynamics shift in predictable ways
- Phases overlap, but there is usually a clear center of gravity
- No one can be certain *if* or *when* 'industrialization' will occur
- Timing major phase shifts requires both *sensing* and *anticipation*
- Different value chain layers are at different lifecycle stages
- Mapping these positions can yield important insights
- Maps help you see and understand the *Why?*
- How well do you *see the board* and *play the game*?

In this chapter, we will discuss how companies can make the technology lifecycle work for their future. The overall pattern of technology evolution tends to be consistent over time, with each evolutionary phase having predictable characteristics that companies can prepare for. By visually mapping their organization's current and future digital landscape, businesses can see the playing field more clearly than their rivals, and then use this knowledge for competitive advantage. The methodologies discussed in this chapter have helped many clients improve both their situational and strategic awareness.

What's the best metaphor for business competition?

A battle?

Following a map?

A chess game?

Sailing or surfing?

Playing poker?

Just as words and language shape the way we think and talk, so metaphors can help us build a mental model of complex situations. As suggested by the figure above, a wide range of quite different metaphors are often used to help us think about business competition, with some of the most popular ones briefly described below:

- **Battle/war.** Sun Tzu's *Art of War* has long served as a useful way to think about business tactics. But today, many people find military language too harsh, so the use of battlefield and war metaphors is declining.
- **Chess.** Strategists often use the chessboard metaphor to highlight the need to think several moves ahead. But business competition is almost never about just two players having precisely the same set of initial resources.
- **Sailing/surfing.** The need to constantly adapt to changing conditions invokes an appealing modern spirit, but business conditions can be shaped in ways that the weather and tides cannot.
- **Poker.** The idea of multiple players betting on different hands – with some cards visible and some not – is arguably the most accurate of these metaphors. But the rules of poker don't change, whereas technology conditions constantly do.

While we use all four of these analogies in various ways, we prefer the metaphor of a *map*. As the Spartans demonstrated at Thermopylae in 480 BC (when the Greeks held back a massively bigger Persian army), seeing and leveraging the competitive landscape can create powerful strategic advantages.

Strategic planning is often too internal and static in nature

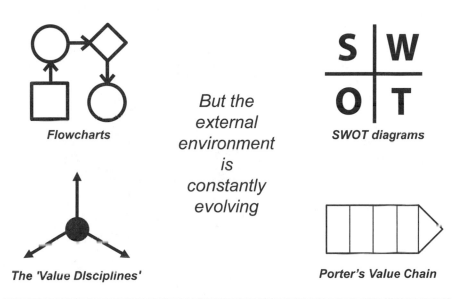

Flowcharts

But the external environment is constantly evolving

SWOT diagrams

The 'Value Disciplines'

Porter's Value Chain

While we tend to use metaphors to think about business competition, for strategic planning we typically rely upon abstract models or frameworks. There are a great many concepts and approaches in the market today, with four of the most widely used depicted above and discussed below:

- **Flowcharts.** Understandably, firms often start with an abstraction of how their business currently operates by developing a detailed *workflow* picture.
- **SWOT diagrams.** For many years, companies have sought to identify and leverage their key *strengths, weaknesses, opportunities,* and *threats*.
- **Value Disciplines.** As discussed back in Chapter 4, this model has helped companies think about whether they want to lead in innovation, efficiency, or customer support, and the important trade-offs implicit in these strategies.
- **Porter's Value Chain.** In his widely used competitive strategy model[16], Professor Michael Porter has long emphasized the need to see the full range of company activity – from inbound to outbound logistics, and everything in between.

Once again, we like aspects of all four of these approaches, especially the emphasis on value. But it strikes us that as a group, they provide a relatively static picture of the internal state of the firm. Given that the technology landscape is always changing, we think that firms need a more outside-in and dynamic approach.

16. Michael Porter, *Competitive Advantage: Creating and Sustaining Superior Performance,* Simon & Schuster, 1985

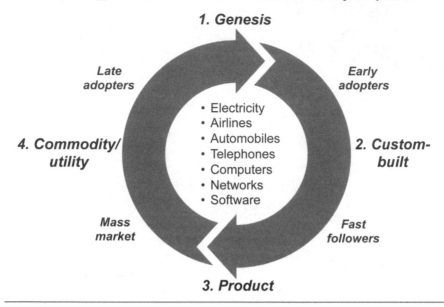

Technology markets evolve in a consistent 'lifecycle' pattern

1. Genesis

Late adopters

Early adopters

4. Commodity/ utility

- Electricity
- Airlines
- Automobiles
- Telephones
- Computers
- Networks
- Software

2. Custom-built

Mass market

Fast followers

3. Product

We believe the nature of digital change is broadly predictable because major technology innovations tend to follow the same *lifecycle* pattern. This means that if you know what lifecycle phase you are in, you can be reasonably confident of what the next phase will look like, even if you can't say precisely when or how this change will develop.

The overall lifecycle pattern is shown in the figure above. Whether we are talking about electricity, computers, or the other industries listed, the cycle is the same. A product is invented *(genesis)*, and its first uses tend to be in niche, application-specific areas *(custom)*. But at some point, it gets stabilized and ready for the mass market *(product)*, eventually becoming a ubiquitous *commodity* product or *utility* service. While this pattern resembles the IT adoption curve of early adopters, fast followers, mass-market customers, and late adopters, as we shall see, there are important differences.

In this chapter, we will emphasize three lifecycle implications. First, we will show that each phase comes with distinct and predictable characteristics that companies can anticipate and prepare for. Second, the shift to the product phase is the key step in enabling any new technology to reach critical mass. Third, the commodity/utility stage is often highly disruptive to existing players, while simultaneously laying the foundation for future genesis. The IT industry demonstrates all three of these patterns, as discussed over the next several pages.

IT industry evolution has closely followed this pattern

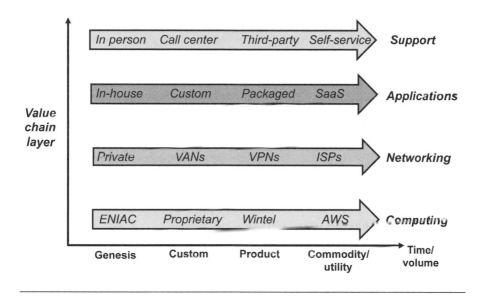

The figure above shows how the IT industry has evolved through this lifecycle model. The pattern has been the same for computer hardware, data networking, software applications, and customer support: systems start off as highly customized/proprietary, but become commoditized over time.

Perhaps the most noteworthy aspect of this figure is that while markets grow in the product phase, they are often disrupted during the commoditization/ utility stage. Consider how Amazon has massively disrupted the traditional computer hardware vendors as well as much of the IT outsourcing industry, just as SaaS vendors such as Salesforce have marginalized much of the traditional packaged-software business.

While product growth and industry disruption are mainstream topics, people tend to underestimate how the cycle of innovation leads directly to genesis. For example:

- Ubiquitous computing has made it much easier to launch new companies.
- Ubiquitous connectivity is making the IoT possible.
- SaaS is now a primary platform for machine intelligence innovation.
- Self-service customer support will pave the way for future agents and bots.

This is what we mean when we say that the nature of technology change is broadly predictable. Looking back, it's hard not to see a high degree of inevitability in these changes.

During each phase, market dynamics shift in predictable ways

	Genesis ⟶	Custom ⟶	Product ⟶	Commodity/ utility
Usage	Experimental	Uneven	Proliferating	Ubiquitous
Mindset	Envisioning	Developing	Deploying	Consuming
Media focus	Hype/wonder	Hackers/makers	Buyers' guide	Applications
Market	Undefined	Taking shape	Rapid growth	Mature
Leaders	Researchers	Entrepreneurs	Companies	'Last man standing'
If fail?	Tolerance	Disappointment	Firings	Penalties
Culture	Exploring	Trying	Using	Procuring
Driver	Curiosity	Sensing	Herd effects	Price/brand

Many readers won't be surprised by the nature of technology lifecycle evolution, or the overall customer adoption pattern. Much of it is common sense. But although it is also common sense that each of these lifecycle stages has distinct characteristics, relatively few companies act on this knowledge. They don't systematically identify the expected future stages, anticipate the corresponding changes in key market characteristics, and then actively prepare for such shifts. As we shall show, we think they can – and should.

The key characteristics of each lifecycle phase are summarized in the figure above. These fundamental shifts in dynamics and behavior reinforce our view that there is no optimal management method or style. Different approaches are needed during each lifecycle phase. For example, so-called *agile* development might be used in the early stages, and then perhaps *Six Sigma* in the more mature phases.

Of the many dimensions shown in the figure, the *mindset* shifts are arguably the most critical. In the early stages of a technology, business management needs to accept and tolerate the inherent risks and uncertainties involved. Conversely, in the later stages of evolution, engineers, IT professionals, and other technical staff often struggle with the shift from *developing* to *procuring*, and the price-sensitive culture that comes with it. Too many companies build things they'd be better off buying, because that's their mindset. It's a common source of inefficiency.

Phases overlap, but there is usually a clear center of gravity

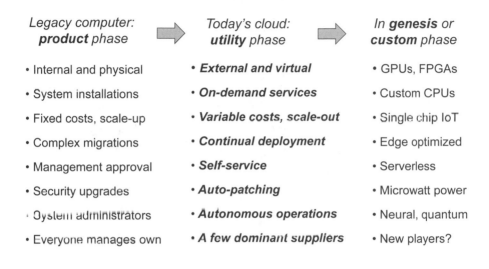

Legacy computer: **product** phase	Today's cloud: **utility** phase	In **genesis** or **custom** phase
• Internal and physical	• *External and virtual*	• GPUs, FPGAs
• System installations	• *On-demand services*	• Custom CPUs
• Fixed costs, scale-up	• *Variable costs, scale-out*	• Single chip IoT
• Complex migrations	• *Continual deployment*	• Edge optimized
• Management approval	• *Self-service*	• Serverless
• Security upgrades	• *Auto-patching*	• Microwatt power
• System administrators	• *Autonomous operations*	• Neural, quantum
• Everyone manages own	• *A few dominant suppliers*	• New players?

Major lifecycle shifts are typically neither sudden nor total. They mostly happen over an extended period of time, during which all four phases are often active. This is the case in the figure above, which depicts today's market for various computing capabilities. Clearly, there is important activity in all three columns, although the utility phase is now the undisputed center of gravity. Each situation is briefly recapped below:

- Within large organizations, the so-called legacy system and/or on-premises market – characterized by the product management practices on the left – is still alive and well, particularly in high-performance areas such as banking, airline reservations, and financial trading.
- But because it dominates consumer and small-business computing as well as almost all new companies and uses, utility computing is the most important form of computer usage today. Amazon and Microsoft (and to a lesser extent Google and IBM) are competing furiously in the management practices listed in the center column.
- Today, IT suppliers are designing new computers and semiconductors tailored to emerging needs such as faster machine learning and low-cost, low-power IoT devices. Looking farther ahead, quantum computing might someday re-invent the computing field altogether. In short, major investments are now being made in both the genesis and custom phases.

This concept of innovation constantly taking place across the entire lifecycle tends to characterize every technology domain: the cycle never really stops.

No one can be certain *IF* or *WHEN* 'industrialization' will occur

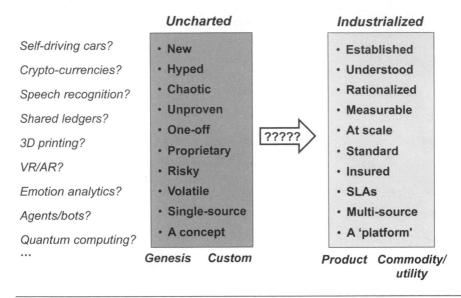

	Uncharted	Industrialized
Self-driving cars?	• New	• Established
Crypto-currencies?	• Hyped	• Understood
Speech recognition?	• Chaotic	• Rationalized
Shared ledgers?	• Unproven	• Measurable
3D printing?	• One-off	• At scale
	• Proprietary	• Standard
VR/AR?	• Risky	• Insured
Emotion analytics?	• Volatile	• SLAs
Agents/bots?	• Single-source	• Multi-source
Quantum computing?	• A concept	• A 'platform'
...	*Genesis Custom*	*Product Commodity/ utility*

As we have discussed, the *nature* of future technology change is much easier to predict than the *timing*. The timing challenge is particularly important during the shift from the custom to the product phase. Such is the importance of this shift that it has earned its own catchy names – such as inflection points and critical mass – and even books – *Crossing the Chasm*[17], *The Tipping Point*[18], and probably others. All are concerned with understanding how products and services advance to the mass-market phase.

We see this challenge through the lens of *industrialization*. By this, we mean the process by which technologies evolve from being uncertain and risky to being proven and reliable, and thus on the path to ubiquitous usage. It's a decisive transition.

As shown in the figure, there are a great many intriguing technologies that are still in the *pre-industrialization* phase. But as stated in the caption to the figure, it's difficult to be certain if or when this industrialization will occur. (But since we believe in these technologies, we think it is much more *when* than *if*.)

Because major advantages tend to accrue to firms that correctly time the industrialization transition, we will further explore this challenge on the next page. We will see that, while we can't be sure when change will come, there are processes that can help organizations anticipate such shifts better than their rivals.

---

17. Geoffrey Moore, *Crossing the Chasm: Marketing and Selling High-Tech Products to Mainstream Customers*, Harper Business Essentials, 1991
18. Malcolm Gladwell, *The Tipping Point: How Little Things Can Make a Big Difference*, Little Brown, 2000

Timing major phase shifts requires both *sensing* and *anticipation*

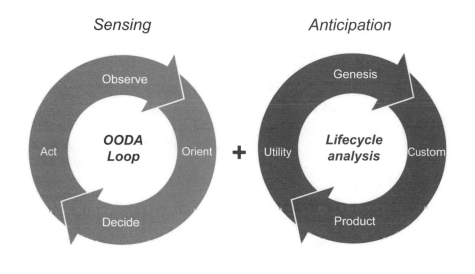

To briefly recap our thinking, the general nature of technology change is predictable, but both the timing and the actual mechanics of change are much harder to discern. This argues for a strong business sensing function, complemented by knowing what to look for. This combination of *sensing* and *anticipation* is depicted in the figure above.

Originally developed by US Air Force Colonel John Boyd in the 1970s, the concept of an *OODA Loop*[19] emphasizes situational awareness, individual/team autonomy, agility, and continual learning, rather than fixed behavioral assumptions. This thinking has long been influential in military, business, law enforcement, and other areas.

In our work, we have sought to combine the logic of OODA Loops with our overall lifecycle model so that organizations can combine *situational awareness* with *situational understanding*. For example, companies should be thinking about how well their sense/respond functions help them to identify the genesis of new ideas, understand relevant customization efforts, and help them time the critical shifts to the industrialization and commoditization phases.

Clearly, the most effective way to apply OODA thinking varies significantly across each of the lifecycle stages – influencing, for example, who you might talk with, what you might read, and what new skills and practices you should be developing. But overall, we think this combination of proactive sensing and informed anticipation can be helpful to just about every organization in its digital strategy efforts. It's an excellent example of a useful military metaphor.

---

19. John R Boyd, *Destruction and Creation*, US Army Command and General Staff College, September 3, 1976

Different value chain layers are at different lifecycle stages

	Genesis	Custom	Product	Commodity/ utility
User needs and experience				
Agents, bots, and NLP				
Automated operations				
Smart products/services				
Databases and analytics				
Messaging and social media				
Market-facing applications				
Production/supply chain				
Internal applications/SaaS				
Identity and authentication				
Mobile and wired networks				
Computing and storage				

In Chapter 5, we defined the key components of the Matrix stack, and provided frameworks with which organizations can assess their current position, particularly in terms of the early adopter/fast follower/mass market/late adopter model. By following that process, companies can develop an overall picture of their firm's Matrix usage, culture, and priorities.

Here, we extend this thinking to take account of ongoing technology evolution. The actual technology landscape that your organization faces is a combination of *where you are*, and *how the landscape is changing*. Imagine that the technology lifecycle is like the four seasons: clearly, the landscape is very different in the spring, summer, fall, and winter, and the way you engage with this landscape needs to change accordingly.

In the figure above, the stack of capabilities shown is mostly for illustration purposes. As discussed in Chapter 5, there are well over one hundred key Matrix services, each with its own nested underpinnings. So, in this exercise, each organization should identify its key internal and external value chain components and their current lifecycle stage.

Clearly, most technologies evolve from left to right, but just as winter gives way to spring, so the utility phase leads to genesis, as today's commodity is tomorrow's *enabling platform*. Consider how ubiquitous electricity made radio, television, and home appliances possible. The IT industry is clearly going through a similar process.

Mapping these positions can yield important insights

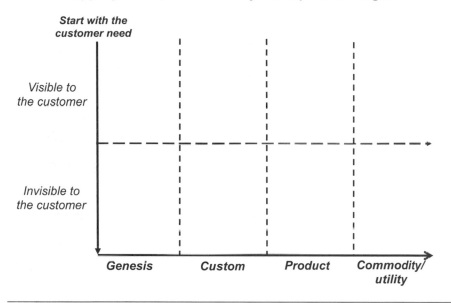

Start with the customer need

Visible to the customer

Invisible to the customer

Genesis   Custom   Product   Commodity/ utility

For many years, we have helped clients systematically plot their activities using value chain maps[20] based on the grid above. In keeping with our overall outside-in approach, we always begin with articulating the *customer need*, and then work backward. We also emphasize the value of distinguishing between value chain components that are *visible* and *invisible* to the customer. To see how the overall process works, consider the types of questions to ask within each area:

- **Genesis.** What experimental efforts are currently underway in your organization? Are they at the right value chain level? When will these efforts shift into the customized offering phase?
- **Custom.** Where are you building customized products and services? Are these efforts providing a real competitive advantage? Could they become – or be replaced by – more industrialized market offerings?
- **Product.** Are your firm's core product offerings at risk of moving into the commoditization phase? Have you shifted from *building* various products to *procuring* them?
- **Commoditization.** What parts of your value chain are commoditizing or shifting to utility services? Are you prepared for the potential disruptions that come with such changes?

Plotting key activities in this way gives organizations a clearer picture of their strategic situation. These *business maps* can greatly facilitate cross-company understanding and communication, while elevating the overall level of strategic discussion. Ideally, they become the main way that an organization sees itself.

---

20. We refer to these as Wardley maps, in honor of their developer Simon Wardley. See https://medium.com/wardleymaps

Maps help you see and understand the *Why?*

How is our industry's value chain evolving?	**How will customer needs be met going forward?**	**Where are we – and our competitors – vulnerable?**
Which strengths can we better leverage?	**WHY ARE WE DOING WHAT WE ARE DOING?**	**Where might new competition come from?**
What role will open source play in our ecosystem?	**What will these changes mean to how we operate?**	**What skills, capabilities, and partners will we need?**

The technology market is complicated and always changing, and this often makes the purchasing of IT products and services tricky. People can't be sure which new technologies will prove useful, and which will win in the market. This uncertainty drives the early adopter/fast follower/mass market/late adopter mentalities: there are only so many people who want to be on the bleeding edge of change, and while many people say they want to be fast followers, this also entails more risk than most want to accept.

This is why IT marketplaces have always had such strong herd effects, as customers understandably seek safety in numbers. As the saying has gone at various times, no one ever got fired for buying IBM, Digital Equipment, or Wintel, just as today there is safety in 'moving to the cloud,' or investing in 'Big Data.' Herd effects strongly reinforce the market's winner-take-all economics.

Value chain maps can help companies become less susceptible to these dynamics. As shown by the questions in the figure, maps make it easier for companies to ask themselves – and develop consensus around – the *Why?* If one can see the future landscape, one can identify desirable positions and strategies, and proceed accordingly. Without some sort of map, organizations can end up flying blind. This close connection between seeing the landscape and developing effective strategies is discussed on the final page of this chapter.

How well do you *see the board* and *play the game*?

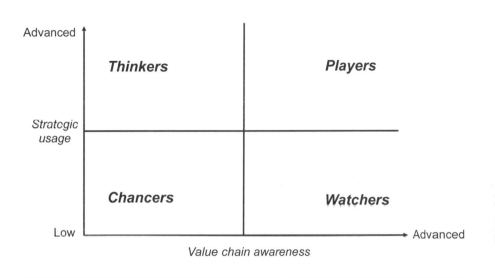

Most firms don't react well to major changes. They either don't see them coming, don't believe what they see, or can't find the will to challenge entrenched beliefs, practices, and cultures. It has ever been thus.

We would never claim that any one methodology can change this by itself, but we have seen many times how the processes discussed in this chapter can help companies willing to embrace them. As shown in the figure, we can summarize the situation today by asking two main questions: *How well does a firm understand its value chain position?* and *How effective is it in using this knowledge for strategic advantage?* These dimensions create four types of companies:

- **Players** see the board clearly, and make effective use of this knowledge.
- **Watchers** see the board, but can't translate this knowledge into action.
- **Thinkers** want to use advanced strategies, but don't see the board clearly.
- **Chancers** really don't think in strategic value chain terms at all.

While there are many firms in all four quadrants, the leading firms of our time will increasingly meet the player criteria. Many already do. But it's important to realize that one doesn't have to be a Matrix giant to be such a player. As at Thermopylae, even a small team can succeed if it can identify the key leverage points. Market landscapes can be a powerful *force multiplier* for firms that can both identify and exploit them.

Chapter 11

The US, China, and a bipolar global IT industry

In this chapter

- What do we mean by 'the IT industry?'
- IT is now the main driver of both economic growth *and* austerity
- Society is becoming increasingly wary of IT's overall impact
- Economics explain why some markets are *winner-take-all*
- Customer service typifies today's relentless digital automation
- But all the jobs aren't going away
- Nations compete for work – and jobs – in many ways
- National IT strategies mostly focus on distinct value chain layers
- The clash of the titans: can China dethrone Silicon Valley?
- We have seen this movie before
- What really happened to Japan in the 1990s
- Can China or India challenge the US and Europe in advanced services?
- An increasingly *bipolar* IT industry is emerging
- Smaller nations often have significant digital society advantages

---

In this final chapter, we will assess the evolution of global IT leadership. We see two main trends: the rise of China, not just as a manufacturer and a vast domestic market, but also as an innovator, determined to challenge the US in many next-generation technologies. However, we also expect that many smaller nations will have important advantages in terms of developing advanced information societies. The result will be much more multipolar demand-side innovation, amidst often fierce bipolar US/China supply-side competition.

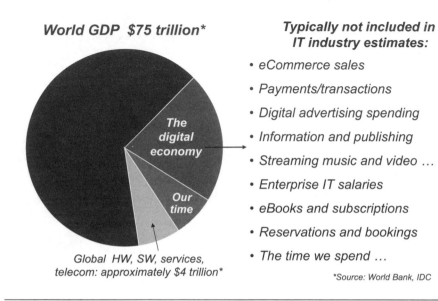

What do we mean by 'the IT industry?'

World GDP $75 trillion*

Typically not included in IT industry estimates:

- *eCommerce sales*
- *Payments/transactions*
- *Digital advertising spending*
- *Information and publishing*
- *Streaming music and video …*
- *Enterprise IT salaries*
- *eBooks and subscriptions*
- *Reservations and bookings*
- *The time we spend …*

The digital economy

Our time

Global HW, SW, services, telecom: approximately $4 trillion*

*Source: World Bank, IDC

A useful first step in trying to assess global IT industry leadership is to define what we mean by 'the IT industry.' As shown in the figure, one can take a narrow or much broader view.

Most research firms and government agencies opt for the former, essentially taking a *supply-side* approach, estimating the value of IT hardware, software, and services sales. The first two of these are relatively straightforward; the last more subjective. Does *IT services* include professional services, training services, distribution services, online services, network services, etc?

But as shown on the right, the IT industry can also be seen to include just about everything that technology enables, and this *demand-side* approach comprises a much larger share of the global economy. Some would even argue that the time we spend using computers should also be counted. As a simple example, if one billion people spend an hour a day online, and we value their time at just $10/hour, this would account for $10 billion/day, or $3.65 trillion/year – roughly the size of the narrow definition above.

The point of this isn't to wallow in the definitional depths, but rather to argue that what we mean by global IT industry leadership is very different, depending upon whether we are taking a supply- and/or demand-side view. In this chapter, we will do a good bit of both, while acknowledging that most people think of global leadership as primarily a supply-side issue.

IT is now the main driver of both economic growth *and* austerity

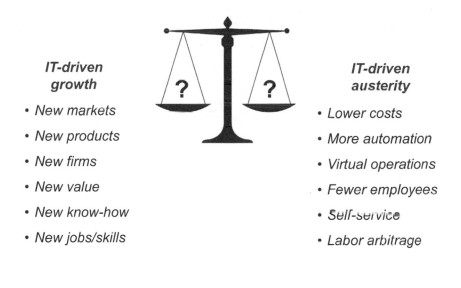

IT-driven growth

- New markets
- New products
- New firms
- New value
- New know-how
- New jobs/skills

IT-driven austerity

- Lower costs
- More automation
- Virtual operations
- Fewer employees
- Self-service
- Labor arbitrage

These supply- and demand-side forces also capture the odd (but intriguing) reality that in today's global economy, digital technology is both the driver of growth and the engine of austerity. The growth comes mostly from the supply side of the industry, as technology companies create new markets, jobs, and prosperity, while the austerity is driven more by the demand side, as organizations use technology to become ever-more efficient.

Thus, the overall impact of technology is clearly a question of balance, and it is here that the rough market size estimates on the previous page take on important additional meaning. Put bluntly, economic growth is heavily associated with the success of digital suppliers, while austerity extends across the much larger demand-side economy.

This doesn't necessarily mean that the net balance is negative. Demand-side efficiencies lower costs, enabling significant increases in total consumption. We believe that this *elasticity* is strong enough to make digital technology a net growth contributor. However, most elasticity effects are almost invisible to society at large, while the use of technology for austerity purposes is often front-page news.

Throughout its history, developed societies have largely accepted that the economic benefits of technology – however hard to see – do indeed offset the more obvious job losses and dislocations. But today, this view is being increasingly challenged, potentially setting up a new era of technology industry skepticism, as discussed over the next three pages.

Society is becoming increasingly wary of IT's overall impact

1. Technology increases income inequality, especially for the 1%
2. Technology is a net job destroyer; MI will make this much worse
3. The *gig economy* undermines workers' rights
4. Internet and social media addiction is widespread
5. We are increasingly under surveillance, with little privacy protection
6. Digital media and algorithms can be easily manipulated
7. Cyber crime is rampant and getting worse
8. Social media is increasing societal coarseness and polarization
9. Silicon Valley lacks diversity and social responsibility
10. Google, Facebook, and Amazon have too much market power

Is all of this true/fair? What, if anything, should be done?

Over the decades, the leaders of the IT industry have gotten used to being lionized – they've been seen as smart, entrepreneurial, passionate, the embodiment of the digital future, and (of course) often unfathomably rich. They have moved freely in the upper ranks of business, celebrity, political, and cultural circles.

But this mingling is getting more awkward, as the overall impact of technology is openly questioned in the areas shown in the figure and more. While one can argue about whether these criticisms are fair, there is enough truth in them that they can't be easily dismissed. For the first time, the US technology industry is on the defensive.

This matters because the dynamism of the US technology sector has been helped by a mostly deregulated environment. But this philosophy is now being questioned. Should internet companies pay more taxes? Do citizens have the right to change what the internet says about them? Should service providers be responsible for the content on their systems? Should Uber drivers be treated as employees? Do antitrust laws need to be more strictly enforced? We could easily go on.

Some of this pushback is the natural result of the extraordinary success that technology firms have had, and some regulatory tweaking could well be useful. But the bottom line is that the technology sector is at risk of a political and cultural backlash, and this is now an important dynamic in global competition.

Economics explain why some IT markets are *winner-take-all*

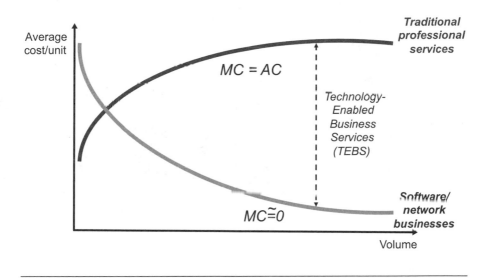

Even though you've heard the statistics – the assets of the world's eight richest people equal those of the 3.5 billion poorest; the top one percent own over half of all wealth; and so on – the numbers can still shock. It's not surprising that such inequality is a major source of societal discontent.

Information technology plays a major part in this – the richest eight include Bill Gates, Mark Zuckerberg, Jeff Bezos, and Larry Ellison (as well as Michael Bloomberg and Carlos Slim). Indeed, inequality is essentially built-in to the underlying economics of the internet, as depicted above. The top curve shows a typical large professional-services firm, say for accounting, law, or consulting. As the volume of business grows, there are initially important economies of scale due to learning and experience, but these eventually flatten out. In economic terms, the marginal cost (MC) comes to equal the average cost (AC) of adding more human capacity.

The lower curve shows how software and network markets are different. Here, the marginal cost of adding a new user to, say, Google or Facebook is close to zero. This means that average costs keep falling with volume, generating increasing returns to scale, and a tendency to create highly profitable, winner-take-all (or near all) industry structures.

In the middle are markets requiring both computer and human interaction. As we shall see, these *Technology-Enabled Business Services* are an important hybrid case, especially in global B2B sectors.

Customer service typifies today's relentless digital automation

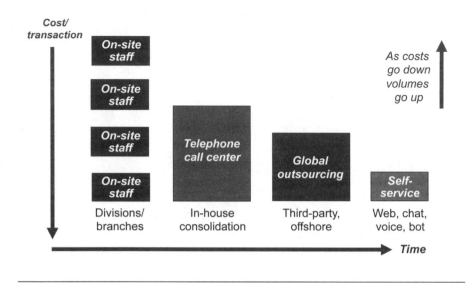

The nature of technology automation – lower costs, higher volumes – is depicted above, using the familiar example of customer support.

For decades, banks, insurance agencies, stores, government offices, and many other businesses supported their customers face-to-face or locally over the phone. But this approach had obvious inefficiencies, especially when service volumes fluctuated. Centralizing support into a shared telephone call center was a natural solution.

However, once this consolidation was in place, it became much easier for the entire customer support function to be outsourced to a specialized supplier. These third parties could serve multiple customers to increase their economies of scale. They could even move work offshore to further drive down costs. While the results were often not very customer-friendly (to say the least), businesses could offload a significant administrative headache, and lower their costs at the same time. Many couldn't resist, despite often high levels of customer dissatisfaction.

Today's internet businesses seek to eliminate human costs entirely, and deliver support through technology-based self-service operations. How many of us have ever talked to a customer account person at Amazon, Google, or Facebook, even once? Technology is the only way that these companies can efficiently support their billions of users, and still provide a generally excellent customer experience. Today's enthusiasm for software agents and chatbots is the natural extension of this trend, although using bots to create a high-quality customer experience remains challenging.

But all the jobs aren't going away

The world needs to:

10 billion people by 2050

1. *Raise global living standards*

2. *Narrow income inequalities*

3. *Modernize national infrastructures*

4. *Expand healthcare access*

5. *Improve care for the aging*

6. *Transform food, energy, and transportation*

7. *Revitalize teaching and education*

8. *Repair/sustain the environment*

9. *Rebuild war-torn and broken nations*

10. *Create entirely new industries/jobs*

There is an immense amount of work to be done all around the world. The real question is: Which nations will thrive?

Customer service is just one example of automation's impact on employment. Retail stores are closing; banks and insurance companies are shedding workers, convenience stores are embracing self-checkout; fast-food restaurants are experimenting with entirely automated operations; and so on. Not surprisingly, many people fear that there won't be enough good, paying jobs to go around.

While such concerns can't be entirely dismissed, similar predictions have been made many times in the past, and have proven wildly, even comically, wrong. And although history doesn't always repeat itself, the evidence thus far also seems reassuring.

To say that 'all the jobs are going away' is really saying that humans no longer have needs that can't be met by machines. But as shown in the figure above, there is a vast array of unmet societal needs. How much of this work can actually be done by machines? And of course, many entirely new industries will surely be created.

Economists often cite Say's Law that 'supply creates its own demand[21].' This doesn't mean that if you make something, people will buy it; it means that the payments needed to build a product or service essentially equal the purchasing power needed to buy it. The challenges above will require plenty of payments, and thus will create plenty of demand, which is why we believe that the question isn't whether there will be jobs, but where the best jobs will be.

---

21. Jean-Baptiste Say, *A Treatise on Political Economy (Traité d'économie politique)*, 1803

Nations compete for work – and jobs – in many ways

Culture	– Language, ideas, knowledge, influence, media
Policies	– Laws, regulations, support, strategies, initiatives
Ecosystems	– Cooperation, know-how, R&D, critical mass
Industries	– Size, share, scale, capabilities, cohesion, agility
Companies	– Competitiveness, leadership, dynamism, reach
Infrastructure	– Physical, digital, financial, political, legal, resource
People	– Education, skills, motivation, entrepreneurism, cost

For much of human history, the primary competition between nations was military. Which country had the strongest armies and navies, and how was this power projected around the world? While military competition certainly continues, the principal form of national competition today is economic. Which nation is doing the best job of generating companies, jobs, and prosperity for its people?

We look at this competition through the seven-layer stack above. We think this model is a particularly useful way to assess global technology competition. For example:

- Which nations have the most skilled programmers, engineers, and workers?
- Who has the most advanced network and related infrastructure?
- Which countries generate global tech companies, and which do not?
- How important and effective are various industrial policies and strategies?
- Where is the national technology ecosystem doing world-class work?
- Are government IT policies mostly effective, or counter-productive?
- Is a nation within the *Anglosphere,* the *Sinosphere*, or on a different path?

These questions make it clear that there is room for a wide range of national strategies and approaches. But taken together, they give us a way of thinking about the exciting but high-stake global technology competition ahead. Over the rest of this chapter, we will use this type of layered thinking to imagine how global technology competition is likely to evolve over the course of the 2020s and 2030s.

National IT strategies mostly focus on distinct value chain layers

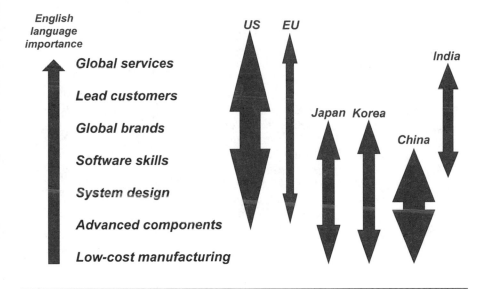

Today's global IT competition can also be viewed from a layered, stack perspective, as different nations/regions tend to have different strengths and weaknesses. Although there are obvious challenges in reducing complex global markets to a single image, we think the overall pattern in the figure above holds true. For example:

- Although China has tremendous strengths in engineering, components, and low-cost manufacturing, it isn't yet as far along in establishing its own global brands as Japan and Korea.
- India is in the opposite position. It is currently weak in systems and hardware and its domestic market lags, but its great skills in software have enabled its IT services firms to become important global players.
- Europe competes across most of the technology stack, but not always as successfully as it would like (hence the thin line). The UK semiconductor firm ARM (now owned by the Japanese firm Softbank) has been a big exception.
- The US has long dominated the IT stack. But can it maintain this status through the next great waves of digital innovation?
- The importance of the English language rises as we go up the stack.

In short, the national strategy of each player is to lengthen and/or thicken the arrows above, as discussed over the rest of this chapter. As suggested by the figure, the most intense competition today occurs in the lower half of the stack.

The clash of the titans: Can China dethrone Silicon Valley?

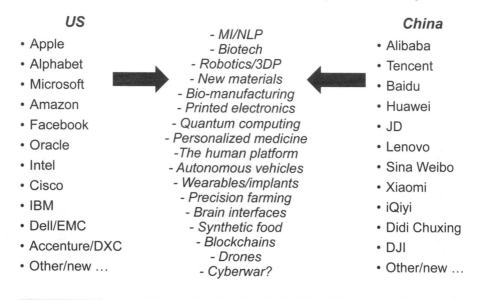

US		China
• Apple	- MI/NLP	• Alibaba
• Alphabet	- Biotech	• Tencent
• Microsoft	- Robotics/3DP	• Baidu
• Amazon	- New materials	• Huawei
• Facebook	- Bio-manufacturing	• JD
• Oracle	- Printed electronics	• Lenovo
• Intel	- Quantum computing	• Sina Weibo
• Cisco	- Personalized medicine	• Xiaomi
• IBM	-The human platform	• iQiyi
• Dell/EMC	- Autonomous vehicles	• Didi Chuxing
• Accenture/DXC	- Wearables/implants	• DJI
• Other/new …	- Precision farming	• Other/new …

- MI/NLP
- Biotech
- Robotics/3DP
- New materials
- Bio-manufacturing
- Printed electronics
- Quantum computing
- Personalized medicine
-The human platform
- Autonomous vehicles
- Wearables/implants
- Precision farming
- Brain interfaces
- Synthetic food
- Blockchains
- Drones
- Cyberwar?

While American firms dominate the global IT industry, China has had two great successes. It's the world's leading high-tech manufacturer, and it has spawned its own set of powerful internet firms. This combination of global supply-side integration and domestic independence is an impressive strategic accomplishment. But China now has much greater ambitions, as it seeks to lead in many of the emerging areas shown in the figure. New markets often do result in new leaders.

Of course, we all know China has great strengths – 1.3 billion people, vast numbers of skilled engineers, a rapidly growing economy, rising wealth, and a strongly supportive state. But it also has major weaknesses – corruption, censorship, environmental degradation, and an often-unreliable legal system. These latter traits can make it difficult for China to attract and retain world-class talent.

Language is also a barrier. The number of people who speak some version of English or Chinese as either their first or second language is roughly the same, but English usage is growing faster. The global dominance of English makes it hard for Chinese firms to move up the stack.

But overall, we expect China to thrive in many emerging technology areas, as will many American and other firms. Borrowing a term long popular in the oil industry, people are now referring to the combined US and Chinese giants – Google, Apple, Facebook, Amazon, Microsoft, Alibaba, and Tencent – as the new *seven sisters*.

We have seen this movie before

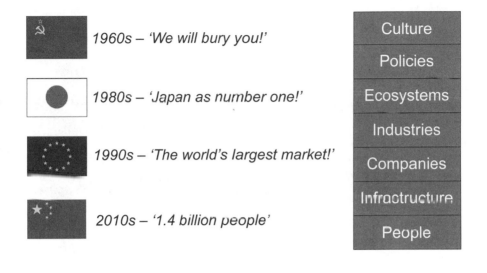

It's almost too easy for Americans to dismiss predictions that China will overtake the US in key technology markets. After all, we've heard similar forecasts for pretty much as long as the IT sector has existed, and they have always been decisively proven wrong. This history is shown in the figure, and briefly recapped below:

- In the 1950s and 60s, many 'experts' proclaimed that Soviet-style centralized five-year planning was the way of the future, essentially endorsing Nikita Khrushchev's prediction that: "History is on our side. We will bury you."
- In the 1970s and 80s, we were told that Japan had developed a superior form of capitalism based on close business/government cooperation, interlocking networks of firms (keiretsu), social cohesion, and long-term thinking. Ezra Vogel's *Japan as Number One*[22] (1979) became an international best-seller.
- In the 1990s, we were told that an integrated European super-state was destined to write the rules of global capitalism, that the Euro would rival or replace the dollar, and that being the world's largest market would prove decisive.

Of course, Japan has had many technology successes and Europe has important IT companies and policies, but none of this has changed global technology leadership. The question is whether things will be different with China. While there are many similarities, China seems to be avoiding the mistakes of its predecessors, as demonstrated by the comparison with Japan that follows.

---

22. Ezra Vogel, *Japan as Number One: Lessons for America*, Harvard University Press, 1979

What really happened to Japan in the 1990s

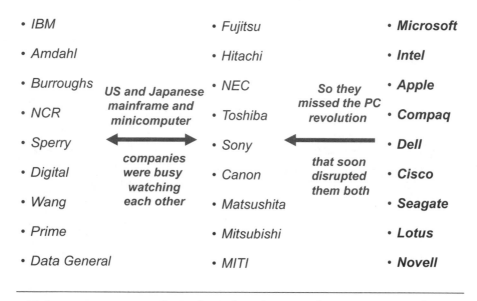

• IBM	• Fujitsu	• **Microsoft**
• Amdahl	• Hitachi	• **Intel**
• Burroughs	• NEC	• **Apple**
• NCR	• Toshiba	• **Compaq**
• Sperry	• Sony	• **Dell**
• Digital	• Canon	• **Cisco**
• Wang	• Matsushita	• **Seagate**
• Prime	• Mitsubishi	• **Lotus**
• Data General	• MITI	• **Novell**

US and Japanese mainframe and minicomputer ⟷ *companies were busy watching each other*

So they missed the PC revolution ⟵ *that soon disrupted them both*

Unless you were actually in the tech industry in the late 1980s, it's hard to imagine how scared the US government and Silicon Valley were by Japan. In one commodity sector after another – memory chips, disk drives, printers, displays, etc. – giant Japanese conglomerates were combining high quality with low prices to put seemingly unbearable pressures on smaller US firms. Their eventual triumph seemed inevitable to many.

But by the mid-1990s, the threat was over. What happened? As shown in the figure, the major Japanese firms were fixated on IBM – and to a lesser extent the other US mainframe and minicomputer companies. They believed that if they targeted the current US leaders, they would eventually defeat them, hence their heavy emphasis on IBM-compatible mainframes, disk drives, PCs, and so on.

But just like IBM and the other US incumbents, the leading Japanese firms failed to see how specialized suppliers including Intel, Microsoft, Cisco, Seagate, and others were rapidly building a new PC-centric IT industry value chain. They also failed to see the decisive role of software – think of the iPod vs. the Sony Walkman.

China isn't making this mistake. While its internet firms do closely track the US leaders (Amazon/Alibaba, Google/Baidu, Uber/Didi, etc.), China also has many well-funded start-ups that are real innovators in emerging technology areas – including software and machine intelligence. It's a major strategic difference.

Can China or India challenge the US and Europe in advanced services?

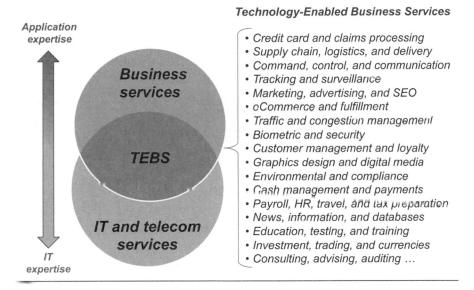

Technology-Enabled Business Services

- Credit card and claims processing
- Supply chain, logistics, and delivery
- Command, control, and communication
- Tracking and surveillance
- Marketing, advertising, and SEO
- oCommerce and fulfillment
- Traffic and congestion management
- Biometric and security
- Customer management and loyalty
- Graphics design and digital media
- Environmental and compliance
- Cash management and payments
- Payroll, HR, travel, and tax preparation
- News, information, and databases
- Education, testing, and training
- Investment, trading, and currencies
- Consulting, advising, auditing ...

As discussed at the start of this chapter, the IT industry can be defined narrowly in terms of its key technology products, or much more broadly to include all the things that IT is used for.

This distinction is particularly relevant with 'services.' Defined narrowly, 'IT services' typically refer to companies such as IBM, Accenture, DXC, Cap Gemini, Infosys, and Wipro, and perhaps telecom services. But when defined broadly, it also includes both consumer services – Google, Facebook, etc. – as well as the Technology-Enabled Business Services (TEBS) shown in the figure. Both markets are critical to the future of global technology competition, but the significance of TEBS is often under-recognized.

Today, TEBS are dominated by US and European firms, but will this change? As of now, we think it's fair to say that China isn't focused on these markets (outside of China), and thus its global prospects do not look strong, although acquisitions are always a possibility.

India, of course, has a much stronger global services position than China, but mostly in back-office *outsourcing*. While becoming a brand-name TEBS supplier is a lesser challenge for India than for China, it isn't easy to establish the strategic customer relationships required. Thus, we expect India to make steady, but not rapid, TEBS gains at a brand-name level, while doing much of the IT work behind the scenes. However, here too acquisitions could certainly accelerate this progress.

An increasingly *bipolar* IT industry is emerging

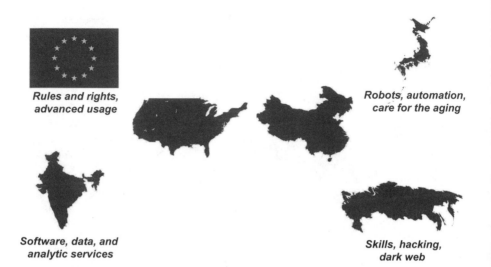

The figure above summarizes our overall competitive outlook, as expanded upon below (apologies to South Korea which could also have been included):

- The US position is currently so strong that some weakening seems inevitable, especially if America's technical education declines and/or Silicon Valley 'hollows out.' But the opportunities ahead are still tremendous.
- China will continue to be globally integrated and domestically independent. It will also lead (and establish its own brands) in many of the key markets of the 2020s.
- India's vast software, data, analytic, and mathematical skills will be essential in building an intelligent planet. It will slowly move up the services value chain.
- Europe will remain a leader in advanced services and usage. It will also help set many privacy, data usage, and competitiveness norms. But the likely loss of the UK will hurt its supply-side competitiveness.
- Japan's need to cope with a declining and aging population will further drive its emphasis on advanced robotics and automation.
- Russia has world-class mathematical and technology skills, especially for IT security. But can these talents be better leveraged outside of the dark web?

In short, the challenge of building an intelligent global economy is so great that the knowledge, skills, and energy of the worldwide IT community are needed. Nevertheless, the coming competition between the US and China will result in increasingly *bipolar* supply-side dynamics.

Smaller nations often have significant digital society advantages

- Sweden
- Norway
- Denmark
- Finland
- Netherlands
- Ireland
- Iceland
- Estonia
- Israel
- Chile
- Taiwan
- Singapore
- New Zealand ...

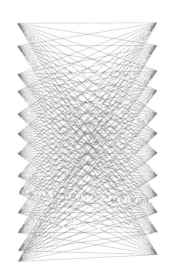

- Wired/wireless infrastructure
- Universal service/access
- Health/genetic records
- Digital IDs
- Smart grids
- Car sharing, self-driving
- Online voting
- Digital cash/payments
- Connected classrooms
- Shared ledgers
- Drone regulation
- Social media regulation
- Privacy/citizen rights

For most of the IT industry's history, the great majority of nations were consumers of IT. Local governments and businesses chose which technology products and services to buy, but they had little influence on how the global IT sector evolved. Symbolically, in the 1970s and 80s, the largest office building in the capital city of many nations was IBM's. Local populations often bristled at this imbalance.

But since the emergence of the web, this dynamic has been shifting. The way that nations and their citizens use the internet varies widely, with most countries having their own important digital players. We expect this shift to accelerate during the Matrix era, as the emerging applications shown above will require complex local implementation.

We believe this argument can be taken further to predict that smaller nations will actually lead in many of the areas listed. The required decisions and investments – and their cultural implications – tend to be much more manageable than in, for example, the US, Japan, and the larger European nations, with their layers of interests, bureaucracy, and complexity.

We look forward to the 13 nations listed above (and many others) serving as laboratories for Matrix innovation. Taken together, they could put a very different spin on what we mean by *global technology leadership*, especially if any significant leapfrog dynamics emerge in the less developed world. The result will likely be diverse multipolar demand-side innovation, amidst increasingly fierce bipolar supply-side competition.

Conclusion

Speaking digital – a lexicon for the 2020s

In this chapter

- The information technology industry has been *consumerized*
- *The Matrix* is becoming a more useful metaphor than *the cloud*
- *MI* is a more accurate term than *AI*
- Unless carefully used, the word *disruption* can be meaningless
- Everyone wants to become a *platform* organization
- Business innovation is shifting from *inside-out* to *outside-in*
- *Cyber, digital* and *information risks* require different defenses
- *IT leadership* and *digital leadership* are not the same
- Enterprise IT plays a consistent set of *4P* roles
- *Double-deep* people are the most employable and promotable
- Innovation is shifting to the *human platform*
- Market leaders leverage the *technology lifecycle*
- Global IT industry competition is becoming *bipolar*
- Business and technology are inseparable and *co-evolving*
- The 2020s and 2030s will see a *triple transformation*

Words matter

In this conclusion, we summarize the key themes of this book by focusing on the relationship between technology change and the language of the marketplace. We will see that the use of certain words naturally tends to shape our thinking and conversations. We have found that when companies adopt the terminology that follows across their organizations, their discussions typically rise to a higher level.

The information technology industry has been *consumerized*

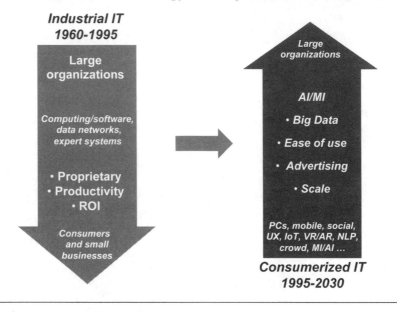

In the 1960s and 70s, IT suppliers focused almost entirely on serving large organizations. Even as the use of personal computers exploded in the 1980s, leading PC makers were designing their products mostly with business users in mind, as evidenced by the mostly bland colors and designs.

But ever since the rise of the internet in the 1990s, the IT industry has become increasingly *consumerized* – a term we coined back in 2004[23]. As shown in the figure, digital innovations now come mostly from the bottom up, with the GAFA giants all firmly rooted in the consumer market.

Looking back, it's hard to over-estimate the impact of this shift. Most of the key technology innovations of recent years – such as social media, digital audio/ video, Skype, Dropbox, Uber, agents, and facial recognition – have emerged in the consumer market first. This means that individuals gain experience in these technologies in their private lives, and can use these often-free advertising-based services at work without the support, permission, or knowledge of their firm's IT organization.

But as important as these changes have been, consumerization is just getting started. Perhaps most importantly, consumer usage is creating the data that makes many machine intelligence advances possible. Looking ahead, innovations in healthcare, wearables, brain interfaces, and the broader human platform will also be consumer-centric. The massive investments needed to serve these billions of global consumers are also the driving force behind the intelligent, Matrix infrastructure this book has envisioned.

---

23. David Moschella, Doug Neal, Piet Opperman and John Taylor, *The 'Consumerization' of Information Technology*, CSC's Research & Advisory Services, 2004

The Matrix is becoming a more useful metaphor than *the cloud*

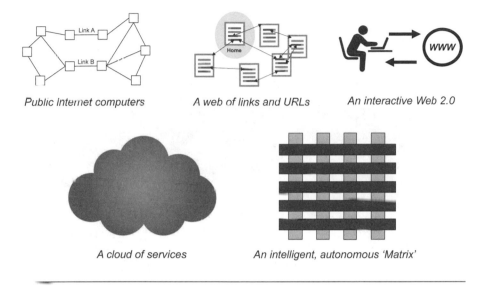

Public Internet computers   A web of links and URLs   An interactive Web 2.0

A cloud of services   An intelligent, autonomous 'Matrix'

Today, even TV commercials refer to 'cloud computing.' While the origins of this term are obscure, its popularity goes back to 2006/7 when Google and Amazon started using it. Before then, we used terms such as the internet, the world wide web, and Web 2.0, as shown in the figure above.

The internet and the web can be defined by their respective communications protocols – TCP/IP and HTTP respectively. But 'Web 2.0' and 'the cloud' are metaphors. The former emerged to capture the desire of consumers to publish their own web content, as opposed to just being passive consumers, while the cloud speaks to the vast array of on-demand digital services available today. Many popular cloud services are so-called *walled gardens*, and not technically even on the internet.

As explained in Chapter 1, we think that the use of 'the cloud' will peak in this decade, as its core metaphor of services 'out there' will be increasingly out of step with the pervasive, embedded, autonomous, and intelligent world of the 2020s, centered around *smart things* and the human platform. Whether 'the Matrix' catches on as a replacement term or not, we think it better captures the post-cloud spirit of these developments.

Today, internet, web, and cloud are interchangeably used, but Web 2.0 has vanished. While 'the cloud' seems unlikely to disappear, there's clearly room for a new term to emerge. In the meantime, we will continue to talk about 'the cloud,' but it's worth remembering that the digital world will be much more than that.

MI is a more accurate term than *AI*

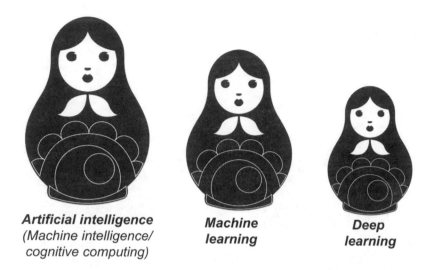

Artificial intelligence
*(Machine intelligence/
cognitive computing)*

**Machine
learning**

**Deep
learning**

Since the 1960s, the term artificial intelligence (AI) has been used in prominent industry conferences, professional journals, research labs, and academic departments. More recently, the IT industry has pretty much standardized on the 'Russian doll' terminology shown above: Deep learning is a subset of machine learning which is a subset of AI (which is sometimes also called machine intelligence or cognitive computing).

As discussed in Chapter 2, we struggle with the word 'artificial.' Literally, it means something 'made by art or skill,' and thus 'not natural,' and in this sense, seems entirely appropriate to the challenge of building intelligent computers. But today, 'artificial' is typically associated with things that are fake, inferior, or an imitation – artificial grass, sweeteners, Christmas trees, etc. The connotations are mostly negative.

We note that people never refer to the 'artificial strength' of a tractor, and the tractor's superior performance in certain tasks is taken for granted. Similarly, we should take it for granted that machines will be superior to humans in certain areas. But just as the tractor isn't a replacement for the body, the machine is not a replacement for the brain.

We think it is telling that, while everyone says 'artificial intelligence,' no one ever says 'artificial learning,' which is close to an oxymoron. As with the Matrix, we think machine intelligence conjures up a more useful image of the possibilities and challenges ahead. While MI seems unlikely to replace AI, it's the more accurate term.

Unless carefully used, the word *disruption* can be meaningless

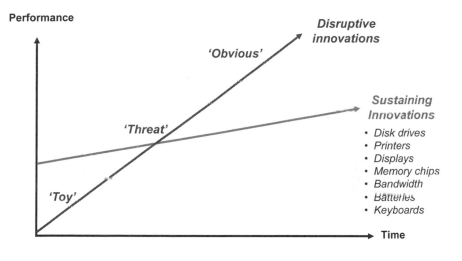

As with artificial intelligence, it's useful to start any discussion of disruption with the dictionary definition. In general English usage, a disruption is anything that 'disturbs an event, activity, or process,' e.g. heavy snowfall disrupting ground and air transport. In this sense, a business disruption can be said to be anything that shakes up the status quo – a power outage, business scandal, new technology, and so on.

But as discussed in Chapter 3, within the IT industry, disruption has taken on a much more specific meaning. As popularized in 1997 by Clayton Christensen, a *disruptive innovation* is one that existing market leaders can't easily respond to. In some way, it doesn't fit into their business model, financial incentives, or organizational culture – often all of the above – and thus it is inevitably led by new players. As suggested by the figure, these new players ride the new technology to eventually replace or substantially diminish the existing order.

This pattern of new markets being led by new players has characterized the IT industry through the mainframe, minicomputer, personal computer, mobility, and internet eras, and shows little signs of stopping. However, in the marketplace today, many of us use 'disruption' in the broader English language sense, while others are Christensen purists. Unless people are clear, the term can be all but meaningless.

Everyone wants to become a *platform* organization

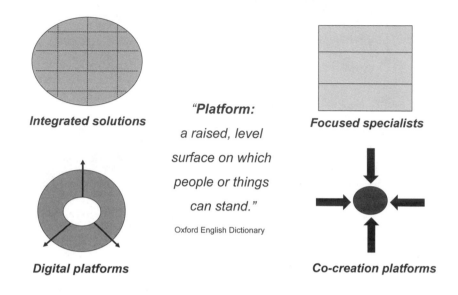

Integrated solutions

"Platform:
a raised, level surface on which people or things can stand."

Oxford English Dictionary

Focused specialists

Digital platforms

Co-creation platforms

While 'AI' was the buzzword of 2017, in corporate circles, the word 'platform' is now equally trendy. As defined above, platforms are merely things one can stand on or build on top of. Why does this trait resonate so well with businesses today?

As suggested at the top left of the figure, many traditional businesses consist of an overlapping set of systems and processes built up and integrated over the years. Here, the desire for platforms is mostly a call for simplicity. Businesses see how the computer industry consists of layers of specialized services, and understand the speed and efficiencies that come with this approach. However, transforming from today's 'hairball' of systems into an *interoperable stack* is typically much easier said than done.

The lower half of the figure depicts an even more fundamental shift. What we call 'digital first' platforms mean that a firm's online presence and capabilities effectively supersede traditional functional, geographic, and product line structures. In such cases, the customer experience and the digital experience are increasingly one and the same. Similarly, the lower right figure suggests how co-creation can harness the energies, skills, and resources of the customer, as Facebook, eBay, Uber, Wikipedia, YouTube, and Airbnb all do.

All four of the above models are explained in detail in Chapter 4, as just about every large firm now seeks to become some form of a platform organization.

Business innovation is shifting from *inside-out* to *outside-in*

Inside-out	➡	*Outside-in*
• Internal capabilities		• Ecosystem resources
• Intellectual property		• Open source collaboration
• Customer consumption		• Customer co-creation
• Marketing programs		• Community/social content
• Packaged software		• SaaS applications
• Company data centers		• Public cloud
• Management/control		• Leadership/influence

In his influential 1937 article *The Nature of the Firm*[24], Ronald Coase argued that the reason companies exist is because their internal transaction costs – planning, coordinating, producing, etc. – are lower than the costs of contracting with the outside world. While this concept is simple, even obvious, transaction cost thinking is still an excellent way of approaching the question of what should be done inside and outside of the firm. In 1991, Coase was awarded the Nobel Prize in Economics.

It is useful to think of today's cloud/Matrix as a means of greatly reducing external transaction costs, since using these services – through browsers, apps, or API interfaces – is often easier, cheaper, faster, and/or better than doing similar things internally, in the areas shown in the figure and more.

Most new firms and small businesses now embrace this mindset, and thus are often outside-in from the start. In Chapter 5, we categorized the overall range of today's cloud/Matrix offerings in order to provide traditional large firms with a way of systematically thinking about how to establish a similar approach as their default operating model.

The need for such thinking will only increase in the years ahead. For many of the key innovations of the 2020s – speech/voice/facial/activity recognition, machine translation, and so on – there won't be a viable internal alternative. Increasingly, interoperable digital services will be seen as the building blocks of the modern organization.

---

24. Ronald Coase, 'The Nature of the Firm,' *Economica* 4 (16), Blackwell Publishing, 1937

Cyber, digital, and information risks require different defenses

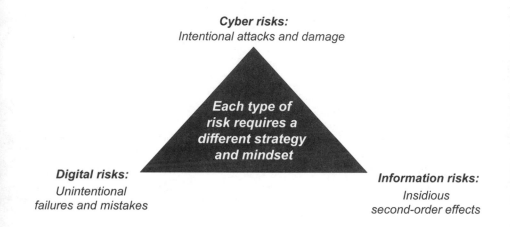

Cyber risks:
Intentional attacks and damage

Each type of risk requires a different strategy and mindset

Digital risks:
Unintentional failures and mistakes

Information risks:
Insidious second-order effects

When business people today talk about technology *risks*, they are usually talking more about *threats*. The difference is important. A logical discussion about risk typically implies a simultaneous discussion of *rewards*, whereas threats are just the potential dangers a company might face. In Chapter 6, we segmented these threats/risks into the three categories shown above:

- **Cyber risks** are intentional attacks from any party, but typically from an external individual or entity engaged in theft, vandalism, sabotage, espionage, exposure, or other damage.
- **Digital risks** are those that stem from unintentional damage caused by errors, misuse, misunderstandings, design inadequacies, or other shortcomings, either inside or outside the organization.
- **Information risks** are typically second-order in nature – such as accumulated system complexity, information overload, system biases and gaming, and/ or the inability of any computer system to fully reflect reality.

Managing each of these threats requires different skills and a different mindset, and companies will benefit by assessing each of these areas separately. For example, today, cyber risks get the most publicity and are primarily the responsibility of security professionals; digital risks are much more common, but they are often covered up or dealt with quietly by management; while information risks are especially insidious because they can be all-but-invisible unless one carefully looks. Once again, using clear terminology can help organizations better think, communicate, and plan.

IT leadership and digital leadership are not the same

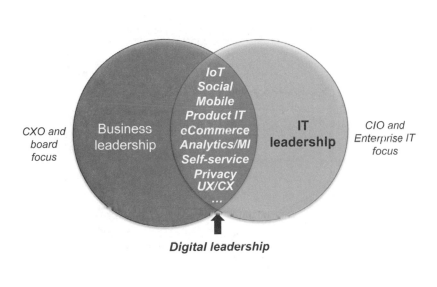

Digital leadership

People often ask us what's the difference between 'digital' and 'IT'? Isn't the former just a more modern word for the latter? We don't think so. Once again, the use of different words signals a significant market distinction.

In most companies today, a good rule of thumb is that what they call 'digital' tends to be those things that aren't primarily run by the IT department. Included are the challenges listed in the middle of the figure, which are often managed by marketing, an engineering organization, or some sort of product or customer group. The need for a team approach in these areas was the main theme of Chapter 7.

Of course, in those firms where the IT organization is particularly successful and forward thinking, it may well play a strong leadership role in these areas. But even here, the pattern mostly holds true. Digital is closely associated with front-of-the-firm customer- and/or market-facing initiatives, while IT is linked to more internal and back-office processes and infrastructure. While both are important, it's clear that digital projects will tend to be more strategic and visible. It's also clear that the overlapped center of the figure above will expand significantly over time.

Just about every client we work with struggles to find the right balance between its business, digital, and IT leadership. It's critical to both the future of the firm and its IT organization, as discussed further on the next page.

Enterprise IT plays a consistent set of *4P* roles

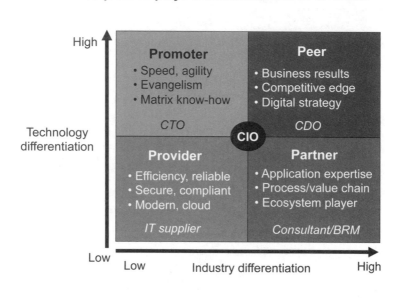

Surely no part of the firm has had more names than the IT organization: the *Data Processing* department, the *Management Information Systems* organization, the *Information Systems* organization, *Central IT, Enterprise IT, Business Services,* and more.   The many names reflect the IT organization's expanding and evolving role.

Over the years, we have helped clients understand and articulate these roles via the 4P model shown above, and explained in much more detail in Chapter 8.   To briefly summarize, an IT organization can distinguish itself in two main ways: by its technical excellence, and by its ability to apply technology to the needs of its firm and industry.   These classifications lead us to four main Enterprise IT roles:

- **Providers** serve as reliable suppliers of agreed-upon IT services.
- **Promoters** advocate the use of new technologies and ways of working.
- **Partners** work and consult closely with the rest of the organization.
- **Peers** have earned a place in the C-suite, and drive the firm's digital agenda.

Importantly, each role requires a different culture, and while most IT organizations will play all of these roles at various times, most also have a clear center of gravity, especially in terms of how they are seen by the rest of the firm. As a rule, Enterprise IT seeks to move up and to the right of the diagram over time. By using this simple *4P* model, companies can build a consensus on the optimal path forward.

Double-deep people are the most employable and promotable

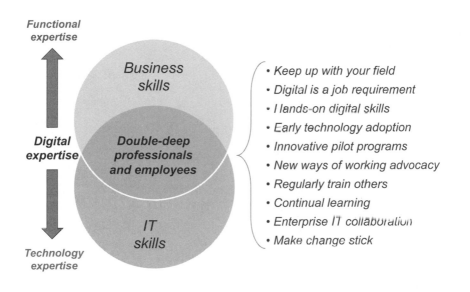

LEF research brings us into contact with many professors and students at leading universities. While the former are mostly interested in our overall technology views and models, students focus primarily on one question: Where will the jobs of the future be?

Today, students are often encouraged to learn coding and other core IT skills. But while it's always helpful to have a better understanding of how computer systems actually work, the fact remains that most people do not have the aptitude, personality, or desire to become a successful software developer or systems engineer. The deeply technical life is not for everyone.

For those who don't see themselves as pure techies, we stress the importance of becoming double-deep. By this, we mean that a good way to succeed in today's business world is to choose the area you want to work in, be it a function – sales, marketing, finance, design, or customer support – or an industry sector – healthcare, financial services, or education – and then learn how to apply technology in that area.

As discussed in Chapter 9, double-deep people tend to be both employable and promotable because they deliver value in all of the areas listed on the right side of the figure. In many cases, they become important de facto leaders in their organizations. In contrast, many single-deep employees increasingly find themselves left behind, with career prospects diminishing over time.

Innovation is shifting to the *human platform*

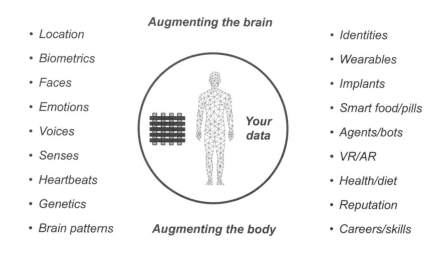

Augmenting the brain

- Location
- Biometrics
- Faces
- Emotions
- Voices
- Senses
- Heartbeats
- Genetics
- Brain patterns

Your data

- Identities
- Wearables
- Implants
- Smart food/pills
- Agents/bots
- VR/AR
- Health/diet
- Reputation
- Careers/skills

Augmenting the body

No area of technology innovation better supports our view that we are moving into a post-cloud era than the emergence of the human platform. Just as the center of IT innovation was once with mainframes, PCs, mobility, and the internet, so will the 2020s focus on applying technology to the human mind and body, in the areas shown in the figure and discussed throughout Chapter 9.

In many ways, our bodies and brains are the last great earthly frontiers. We know so little about the way we walk and talk, or the rhythms of our breathing and heartbeats, and we are only beginning to see how our senses and strengths might be augmented through implants, prosthetics, and nutrients. The eventual healthcare, quality of life, and human performance possibilities will be extraordinary.

The frontier of the brain has even greater possibilities, as we know even less about how we think, and why we feel and behave as we do. The ability of MRI technologies to literally see what is going on inside our own heads promises to change many forms of training and education, and even the way we think about ourselves.

Machine learning is a key common denominator. It will be used to detect patterns, changes, and anomalies in all of the physical areas above, while also giving us a better sense of both how the mind works, and how human and machine intelligence can be successfully brought together.

Market leaders leverage the *technology lifecycle*

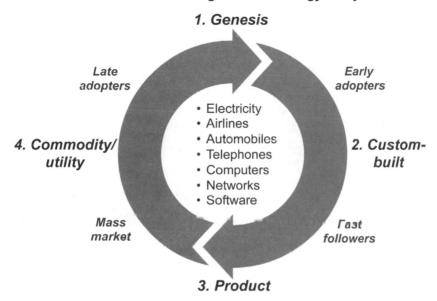

1. Genesis

Late
adopters

Early
adopters

**4. Commodity/
utility**

- Electricity
- Airlines
- Automobiles
- Telephones
- Computers
- Networks
- Software

*2. Custom-
built*

Mass
market

Fast
followers

3. Product

As will be expanded upon later, one of our key working assumptions is that business and information technology are inseparable, and co-evolving. This means that many of the dynamics within the technology industry are now becoming business dynamics as well. One of the most important examples of this is the *technology lifecycle* pattern shown in the figure above.

In all of the industries listed in the center of the figure, the development pattern has been the same. A technology is created (genesis) and is only used by a few early adopters. But as the technology improves, it starts to be used for various niche and customized applications, attracting influential fast followers. Then at some critical point, the technology becomes a sufficiently proven and standardized mass-market product. Eventually, it matures into a ubiquitous commodity or utility service.

But importantly, the pattern doesn't stop there. Today's utility service is tomorrow's platform for innovation. Consider how ubiquitous electricity enabled radios, television, and home appliances; or how ubiquitous connectivity enabled social media, which itself now enables all manner of specialized communities. The cycle never stops.

As discussed in Chapter 10, the challenge for businesses today is to bring this *lifecycle thinking* into their strategic planning processes. Since the pattern of technology evolution is so consistent, the nature of future business changes can be broadly anticipated and prepared for, even if the timing often remains uncertain.

Global IT industry competition is becoming *bipolar*

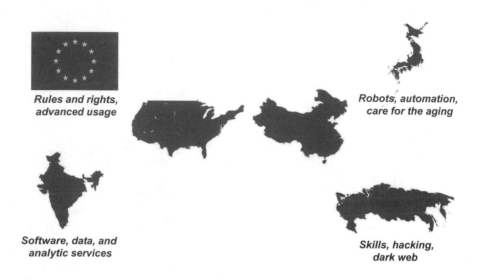

Rules and rights,
advanced usage

Robots, automation,
care for the aging

Software, data, and
analytic services

Skills, hacking,
dark web

The US has dominated the high-tech world for so long that it's easy to take it for granted. During the late 1980s, many predicted that Japan would assume leadership, but their hopes faded as the personal computer and internet eras unfolded. Today, many expect that, because of its great size, rapid growth, and intense focus on technology and education, China will eventually prevail.

As discussed in Chapter 11 and implicit in the figure above, we view China's rise through the lens of a future bipolar global IT industry. China will continue to thrive in high-tech manufacturing; it will dominate its huge domestic market, and it will be a leader in many emerging technology sectors; but this leaves equally large opportunities for the US and others in the trillion-dollar IT marketplaces to come.

While the digital world will revolve around the two poles, important contributions will come from all over the globe. Because of its ability to bring vast software skills to the Anglosphere, we think India will be particularly influential over time. Should the US/India high-tech industries stay as synergistic as they are today, their combined heft could be more than enough to offset the Sinosphere in many areas.

But while the titans battle it out, many smaller nations will become digital leaders in their own right. As explained in Chapter 11, more cohesive and manageable nations will have many advantages in building the intelligent digital societies we envision.

Business and IT are inseparable and *co-evolving*

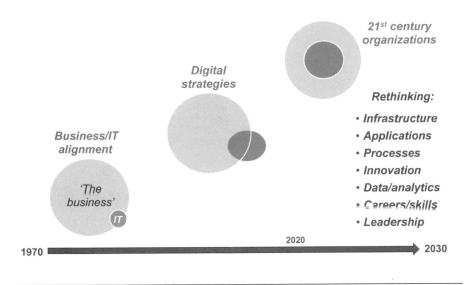

For over a decade, we have used the figure above to depict the changing relationship between large organizations and information technology. Whereas initially, the IT organization was an odd outgrowth of 'the business' – with separate people, speaking a separate language, and often in a separate building – technology has become ever-more inseparable from the operations of the firm.

Today, we are still at an interim stage, and thus we don't have a final picture of what the eventual *nature of the firm* will be. While we could take today's Matrix giants as likely models, as these companies tend not to make many physical products, their experience applies to some industries more than others. Additionally, we can already see that Google, Amazon, et al face many of the same challenges in management decision-making, human resource development, employee morale, and organizational structures that traditional firms have always had. This suggests that, from a human relations perspective, the firms of the future will be recognizable to business leaders today.

What will be very different is the way that most work gets done. When we say that business and IT are co-evolving, we mean that new technologies inevitably require new management practices. Taken together, the changes that stem from the systematic use of modern technologies across all the areas listed above comprise a good definition of what we mean by digital transformation, as briefly recapped on this book's final page.

The 2020s and 2030s will see a *triple transformation*

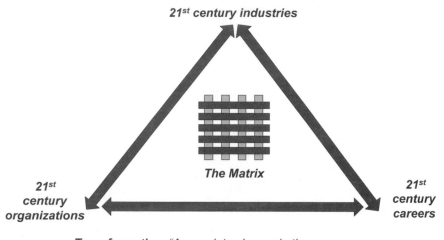

21ˢᵗ century industries

The Matrix

21ˢᵗ century organizations

21ˢᵗ century careers

Transformation: "A complete change in the appearance or character of something or someone, especially so that that thing or person is improved" – Cambridge Dictionary

In this concluding section, we have stressed the importance of clearly defining commonly used terms such as disruption, artificial, risk, and platform, and the same can certainly be said about transformation. In looking at the dictionary definition above, we think the key phrase is 'complete change.' While it's a pretty high bar, it's not an unreachable one. Consider that:

- The intelligent digital infrastructure this book has described is becoming the center of gravity within just about every *industry*, as value increasingly migrates to the digital world. Many sectors have already been disrupted, and the technologies of the 2020s are well suited to challenge those which have not.

- While human leadership and learning will remain as vital as ever, digital-first *organizations* work quite differently than most large firms today. The recent focus on becoming 'a platform organization' is a precursor of the many changes to come, as companies seek to become more outside-in and co-create value with their customers.

- Digital technologies will become increasingly vital to most of our *careers*. Many of the best jobs in the coming years will be those that combine deep subject matter knowledge with the relevant technology skills. In these double-deep areas, the opportunities seem almost unlimited.

Taken together, we hope that *Seeing* this triple transformation of industries, organizations, and careers will help readers prepare for the exciting opportunities of the 2020s – and beyond.

Index